£1. 65

A Strachey Boy

RICHARD STRACHEY

A Strachey Boy

EDITED AND WITH A FOREWORD BY
SIMONETTE STRACHEY

PETER OWEN · LONDON

ISBN 0 7206 0571 7

PETER OWEN LIMITED
73 Kenway Road London SW5 0RE

First published 1980
© Simonette Strachey 1980

Printed in Great Britain by
Daedalus Press Somers Road Wisbech Cambs.

FOREWORD

My husband, Richard Strachey, was in the middle of writing his autobiography when he died in 1976. He had completed a manuscript of 200,000 words.

Last year, under the title *A Strachey Child*, I published the first part of this manuscript complete. *A Strachey Boy* takes the author's story up to the end of his prep school days at the age of fourteen. Owing to present-day difficulties in publishing long books, it is an edited version of the rest of the manuscript. The complete typescript is available in the British Library for those who are interested in reading it.

The present volume can be read quite separately from *A Strachey Child* since it begins with a great change in the author's life: the setting-off to his first boarding school. Nevertheless, some notes on his family background may be of interest.

Richard Strachey, always called Dick, was the son of Lytton Strachey's brother Ralph who worked in India as civil engineer to the East India Railway. His mother, Margaret Severs, was a headstrong beauty who met Ralph while she was on a visit to her brothers in India. Her thoughtless, flamboyant behaviour was the exact opposite to that of the reasonable Stracheys. Dick was born in 1902 and spent his first three years in India; he was followed by two more children, John and Ursula. Since Ralph spent most of his life working in India and Margaret was always on the move between her husband and her children, there was no established family home. Houses were rented in Hove and run by a small number of almost permanent servants – the two sisters Cookie and Mabel, Old Nanny, and the housekeeper Mrs Podmore, nicknamed Prodgers, a brisk American who soon became the mainstay of the household.

After weathering the storms of growing up Dick became a writer. Perhaps his best known and most loved works are his books for children, the 'Little Reuben' and 'Moonshine' series.

I should like to thank John Hounam for his advice and very great encouragement while we worked together on the manuscript.

Simonette Strachey
February 1980

CHAPTER ONE

I set off for Beaudesert Park with my mother calmly enough. After all, it would take me the whole day to reach it. There would always be another corner to turn, another long road for the tumbril to travel, another corner, another road; and much might happen before we reached the place of execution. We might have an accident. We might get ill. We might miss a connection. We might get carried on to Crewe. We might even escape altogether. Anything could happen in a train and there was no need to be unduly pessimistic. But we remembered to change at Birmingham, and the porter there put us into the train for Henley-in-Arden; and having studied the map and Bradshaw, I began to see that time was running out. I had waited on events: now I must act. In first class carriages without corridors a lavatory was provided; and my mother, no doubt to prepare herself for the meeting with my new headmaster, Mr Richardson, and his wife, retired into it. As soon as I heard the door lock (an unnecessary precaution) I wriggled under the seat and vanished. It wasn't particularly clean – even I noticed that – and not especially comfortable; but I was thin enough to fit in all right. I only had to keep quiet, and be careful not to sneeze, and with any luck that train would leave my mother at Henley and get me back in time for supper at Hove. But the best-laid schemes o' mice and men gang aft a-gley.

Margaret returned into an empty carriage, and now the fun would begin. She gave a gasp of surprise, sinking on to a seat, and I almost laughed aloud at her astonishment. Where was Moses when the light went out? Where was her Dickey-boy? In the dark, of course, and she'd never find me. But then everything went wrong.

7

Instead of taking it as a good joke she suddenly began to cry and her lamentations convinced me that she thought I had fallen out. I began to see that I had not fully considered all the consequences of my little game. I should find it hard to listen to poor old Mumbo-Jumbo sobbing and sighing all the way to Henley-in-Arden for her mangled boy when that boy was comparatively comfortable under the very seat she was occupying. I could not bear to think of her being unhappy. With the worthy thought that I must at once put an end to her misery another, less worthy, entered my mind and convinced me that I should reveal myself before worse occurred. At any moment now she was bound to read that wretched notice: 'In case of EMERGENCY pull the cord. Penalty for improper use, £2.' She might consider this to be an emergency. The train would stop, the guard would appear, and I should look a proper fool to say the least of it. So, once again, and less painfully, I popped out between her legs; and the scream of fear and rage with which she greeted my arrival was a satisfactory relief from those dismal moanings. There was little time for much rebuking but enough, in that ill-omened lav, for plenty of scrubbing and washing which reduced *me* to tears, so that the Richardsons welcomed two red-eyed guests on the platform; and as they made no comment on our condition I expect it was one they had often met with before – but probably for different reasons.

We had a very good tea at which I made the acquaintance of Austen Richardson, a heavily built boy of about my size though a year younger. He was on the verge of being promoted to his father's school but at that time inhabited the nursery; and there, already an accomplice of his parents, he introduced me to some of his toys which I thought rather better than mine, especially a No. O gauge clockwork train. I was not allowed to wind it up, still less to put it back on the rails after it had come off. But the object of all these conspirators was achieved, and my attention so much engaged, that Margaret was able to slip away without the pangs she might have suffered from a last farewell. I have generally been able to accept a *fait accompli* with less outcry than one still in the balance; but when Miss Whatley, the matron, came to lead me off to my dormitory, and when she gently told me my mother had had to fly to catch her train, I suddenly realized that I had come very far afield and was quite lost and alone. I gave way to tears. She did her best to console me by pointing out that none of the other boys had their mothers at school with them and didn't mind at all. I didn't care whether the others minded or not. The fact remained that I did. But when she told me, taking me by the hand, that she would be a mother to me, I began to see things in a more cheerful light. Clutching on to that hand of hers I entered the dormitory without any outward signs of distress, though nearly deafened by the uproar of seven small boys in a state of riot. This was an instant relief to me. Thanks be, I was among monkeys not monks.

As we entered a paper dart fell provocatively at our feet. I disengaged myself from my protectrice, seized this weapon and hurled it back whence it had come: a shallow reaction, I suppose, for one so recently bereaved and my only excuse – unjustifiable with the grave and constant – must be, as on, alas, too many and more serious crises in my life, that I was always ready to dismiss the tragic and grasp at anything that might serve, *pro tem*, to efface it. And besides I am easily tempted. Miss Whatley was not displeased with this effort, and even smiled. But she had authority enough to quell the inhabitants of that zoo. I remember her very words: 'Off with your clothes and into bed.'

With real shame I have to admit that I did not know how to undress, let alone how to dress, and I found myself standing, fully clothed, by my bed while the others, safely in theirs, were at liberty to laugh at my immobility. Miss Whatley, however, was an understanding woman; and remarked, while she removed my clothes, that there had been a time when George, Horace, Simon, the other Horace, Fabian, John and David had been just as helpless. In a day or two, she told them, Dick would probably be faster than Simon or David and neater about folding his clothes than either of the Horaces. So much for that little gang. Yah! My bed was next to her room, three steps down into it; and I was told to knock on her door if I wanted anything. Quite a day, and I went to sleep at once. But could not Margaret have warned me that most schools lacked old nannies? And could she not have prepared me for the ritual of getting into bed? No, not Margaret.

I don't know why I arrived at Beaudesert Park several days after the term had begun. This delay, however, was very fortunate and contributed to introduce me gently to what might have been the intolerable regularity of school life. I must make it plain that, entirely owing to Sir, it never became either regular or intolerable; and I met with an instance of this broad-minded attitude of his immediately after breakfast. The gabble of twenty-three small boys was hushed for a moment as he bowed his head (I saw them bow theirs, so I bowed mine, too) and announced in one and the same sentence:

'For what we have received may the Lord make us truly thankful there will be a whole holiday.'

Val, only by courtesy the head of the school since his functions were never defined and his authority never recognized, a youth of thirteen, leapt to his feet and led us in our response:

'Three cheers for Mishter'n'mishes Richerson!'

'Hip, hip, hooray!'

Oh, what a wonderful school I had come to. Three cheers for Beaudesert Park! Nor were we sobered by Miss Whatley's stern command:

'Lavatories first, boys.'

Matron was correct in her use of the plural 'lavatories'; but only just. One of them was an appendage of the box-room and known as the indoor lav. The other was attached to the Playground, favoured by the gardener Hopkins and his boy, and used by us with some reluctance; especially in winter. We called it the Black Hole of Calcutta, but it was referred to as the outside lav by our elders. Both of them, I mean not only the seats, were absolutely filthy. Layer after layer of shit was daily added to the encrustments of ages and both floors were always awash either from dripping cisterns or pissing cocks. I suppose Hopkins' boy, whose job it was to attend to such matters, gave it up as hopeless as soon as term began. During the hols he might have planed the seats down a bit – but he was no Hercules and there was no river Alpheus at hand to cleanse those Augean stables. The same state of affairs prevailed at Rugby; and after some eleven consecutive years of lavatory conditions that disgusted me from the very beginning and to which I never became reconciled, I have almost always approached an unfamiliar seat with gingerly precautions.

I have never been so proud as to believe that the natural order of events has, in any particular instance, been altered especially for my benefit; and I wonder why my first day at school should have been a holiday. It may have been that after the stress of that first week of a new term Sir himself had need of a break. He was more at home in the great outside than ever he was within four walls. He had a keen interest in all sport from huntin' and shootin' to golf;

and he was so notable a cricketer that he was still called upon from time to time to play for Warwickshire. He may have felt that it was a shame to be 'kept in' on such a beautiful September day; or he may have wanted to show Mr Nathan, his assistant, that if he knew almost nothing about Maths or any branch of Science he could probably drive a golf ball twice as far as that rather ineffectual young man. The Park was large enough for both football and cricket pitches; and, by courtesy, a golf course. It was smaller than the usual kind and rather monotonous since it only consisted of two holes – one there and the other back. But, if persistent, a round of eighteen holes could be accomplished. There was only one green by the great Chestnut Tree, since a small portion of the cricket pitch served as the other and was kept at all times well rolled and mown, by us, for Mr Richardson's convenience. Mr Nathan was slightly more accurate on the greens – I think, like my father, croquet should have been his game – but without avail since his formidable opponent always had many strokes to spare. No match between them ever lasted for more than ten holes since even Sir could calculate that being ten up with eight to play Mr Nathan had no hope of winning.

We were at liberty on that day to choose between working our gardens (each one yard square), dug reluctantly once a year by Hopkins, and collecting conkers under the Chestnut Tree. So, armed with sticks, we congregated beneath the Chestnut Tree in company with the cows. They could put up with the cawing from the rookery; but the yells of small boys, the sticks and conkers that fell on them, the bombardment from the golf balls disturbed their repose and they moved off to become a hazard on the fairway, leaving behind them many booby traps into which their enemies uncaringly slid and fell. I was a little shy at first but was soon as busy as the others, and in next to no time was even boasting that I had got the largest conker anybody had ever seen. This was open to question since all of them made the same claim for theirs. I might have been downcast at the universal cry, when I showed my treasure to them, of 'Rot!'; except that no conker was ever agreed to be the largest, and all such assertions were summarily dismissed with that new and scornful exclamation. Another word, which I added at once to my vocabulary, competed feebly with the first.

'Here's a whacker! Look!'

'Rot!'

'Sooty's got a whacker!'

'Rot! He can't even throw!'

'Must have found it in a cow-pat.'

'Didn't.'

'You did.'

'Anyhow, it's rot, not half as big as mine.'

'Rot!'

'Whackers are no good. They bust quicker than small ones.'

'Rot!'

'Char! Char! Char!'

'Rot! Rot! Rot!'

This was meat and drink to me; and I shall never forget the exhilaration of that first day of my bondage and my freedom. I was one of a crowd, indistinguishable to the adult eye from my fellows; part of a swarm and no longer the Queen Bee. Although I might not have quite understood what was happening to me then it was as if a great burden had been removed from my shoulders. I seemed to have escaped once and for all from the swaddling clothes of infancy, from the restrictions of the nursery and from the prejudices of a mother who saw in her children no more than an extension of her own personality. I now looked down at my splashed shoes and stockings without dread; indeed, with an exulting smile. There were twenty-three of us in the same condition, twenty-three of us to be rebuked – not just one.

'Miss Whatley tells me, Harry, that the boys are disgracefully dirty.'

'Well, yes, my dear, I suppose so. Rascals!'

'I should have thought that you and Mr Nathan –'

'I'll speak to Mr Butcher about those cows. He can put them in the Railway Field. Mr Nathan might have halved the seventh if he hadn't been stymied. Brutes!'

'The Chestnut Tree had better, in the meantime, be put out of bounds.'

'Certainly. Hear that, you maddening little animals? Tree's out of bounds. We'd better have a football match this afternoon. Your turn for ref, Nathan.'

'I took it on Saturday. I'm testing the bike on Liveridge Hill. Got a new carburettor.'

'Can I help push it this time, Mr Nathan?' (chorus from the whole school).

'I think, if Mr Nathan requires assistance with his machine, he would be better advised to employ Hopkins. Our boys are too delicate for that sort of work, as you know, Harry.'

'Well, yes, my dear, I suppose so. Rascals!'

'And remember, Harry, Sooty is not to play anywhere except in goal; and Horry is not to play at all. Fabian and Max are to take out their plates before the game. And I think Dick had better watch with Horry.'

'Hear that, boys? And don't you forget it.'

'Oh, please, Mishes Richerson, can't I play, too?'

'That boy's keen, my dear; it won't do him any harm, surely?'

'You must have heard what his mother said yesterday. He's far too weak to be on the run all day long.'

'I wouldn't run about much in goal, would I, Sir?'

'True enough. What about goal, Margery?'

'Have it your own way, my dear. If you know better than Matron and Dr Agar –'

'I'm not saying I do, Margery. From the look of him he might become a centre-forward. But if you want him in goal, well and good. For what we have received may the Lord make us truly thankful amen. Now get changed, you rascals.'

Perhaps I should say something about our health as it might be thought that I had come to a school for invalids. We suffered vicariously for our parents. It was they who were ill, most of them seriously; but, a little eccentricity apart – understandable under the circumstances – we were an average lot and quite as normal as the peculiar phobias of our mothers and fathers allowed us to be. We must consider, too, that it was a social distinction at that time, to be blessed with children who were different and naturally required special attention. Among hundreds of prep-schools there was plenty of room for those that catered for 'delicate' boys, and Margery Richardson, if not Arthur Harry, had been clever enough to cash in on the demand. So Beaudesert Park flourished and even its numbers increased as time went on, but it always remained a small school and a welcome depository for the sons of the afflicted. Margery's fussy regulations might have damaged us permanently, as they followed along the lines we were used to at home; but luckily, Sir, who was only a great boy himself, was there to frustrate and neutralize her sycophantic encouragement of our parents' neuroses; and, though he was never aware that he was doing so, it was due to him and not to Margery, still less to Dr Agar, that we enjoyed an almost permanent state of *mens sana in corpore sano*.

Before the game began Sir collected plates and spectacles from those who wore them, not without protest from Gerald.

'I can't see without my specs, Sir.'

'Rot! You can see a football, my boy; or, if not, you must be blind.'

'Yes sir.'

'And look here, Val, what on earth is Dick doing wandering about the field like that?'

'I don't know, sir. Get into goal, you fool – and not Sooty's. Your own, this one.'

I retired to the other goal. There were some fanatics among us who were able to sustain an enthusiasm for the game, but for the most part our interests were engaged in the attempts of Hopkins and Mr Nathan to get his 'Indian' into action down the drive. When, at last, after a series of explosions, Mr Nathan got going, there was loud applause; and at this moment our side scored the only goal of the match. I don't think I touched the ball during the whole afternoon. It was enough for me to be taking part in a real game of football. Dickey-boy was plain Dick (until Sir and the others had had time to garnish me with nicknames), that big boy Val had condescended to include me in the rank of fools, I had been collectively addressed as rascal and maddening little animal; and I was clearly accepted everywhere as one of the herd. How happy and safe I felt to be a boy among boys! In less than twenty-four hours I had been metamorphosed from a grub into a butterfly. I had burst my way out of the dark chrysalis of infancy towards order and light. At last there would be room enough to spread my wings.

I have always been at the mercy of a passionate heart too little governed by an admiration for the severities of logic and reason; though I have, on occasion, tempered my feelings, or rather damped them down, by taking thought. My loves and my hates, my fears and my lack of caution, so impetuously pumped through my veins, have often got me into trouble; and I'm aware that a proper balance between emotion and reason, could it have been my lot, might have earned me a smoother passage than I have had. But I don't regret the winds I have raised. There is excitement in a storm, and something very like boredom in a flat calm. I have never been so spiritless, so low, as when circumstances have forced me to pursue the even tenor of my way.

It is not surprising that, genealogically, I should have reacted to events in a highly irregular way. My mother was far from stable; and the Stracheys, although they were much better qualified to preserve a reasonable attitude to life, were far from being the cold fish the general public thought them. They did not, if they could help it, ever display their emotions. But their intimates were only too well aware that they had them. Their need for love and light was not so explosive or obvious as that of my mother. The way of the basking shark, disporting itself on the surface of the deep, was not theirs. They had much more in common with the weaver fish, a creature that lurks in the shallows round our shores, covers itself with a warm blanket of sand, and greets the unsuspecting bather with a formidable and poisonous sting – but only if it is disturbed. The Stracheys were, of course, often disturbed. Such charity as they had – and they must have had a good deal to tolerate *me* – did not extend to dullards and dunces; though, professionally, some of them learnt to be patient. Pernal, as Principal of Newnham, would have had plenty of practice in an art that even Pippa acquired only with the utmost difficulty – and both of them could give a severe nip whenever they felt like it. The others, immune from the good-natured irascibility of the lower orders, would turn on the importunate when there was no alternative way of escape and paralyse the aggressor with a remark tipped with poison. I don't think they fully realized the deadly powers they possessed in the art of humiliating an opponent or a bore. If they had been merely rude or cruel or gross the wounds they inflicted would not have festered, and a lesser portion of disgust and aversion would have been their lot. A tincture of wit generally accompanied the blow, and that was fatal for their reputation in a century remarkable for the dullness of perception and humourless benevolence of the common man – a perception and a benevolence that led to the slaughter of a hundred millions of them.

The little côterie of Bloomsbury, in which the Stracheys moved and had their being, required few contacts with the outside world, sought no proselytes, and was happy in the enjoyment of its own conceptions of the good life. They were highly suspicious of strangers and those who collected scalps. If they were to be known

to the public at all, it should be by their works and not in person –
though, eventually, this narrow principle was relaxed and the less
austere among them achieved a certain notoriety, and even fame.
During this later period Lytton, who was always much more of a
bohemian than a snob, became too often a butt for bores. I was
standing next to him at a party when a young American, fortified
with drink and the best of intentions, accosted him recklessly:

'Say, Mr Strachey, I've come all the way over the Atlantic just
to see you.'

'Well, now you have; so you can go all the way back again.'

I was delighted with this savage retort which instantly annihil-
ated the dinosaur; and, in the crush of a social gathering, what
other escape presented itself to poor Lytton?

Marjorie, in my view, was by far the most brutal of them all. Her
rebukes were delivered with the force of a sledge-hammer and the
dunce was lucky, one felt, to escape with his life. She could love as
violently; and did not hesitate as a young girl to carve on her arm
the bloody initials of another young person at the same school.
(And, oddly, it transpired in later years that her beloved was the
mother of my first wife.) But she would also take to flight on occasion. A great crush on a girl friend – the two of them were to tour
Europe on bicycles – was hopelessly punctured the very first night
of their arrival in Brussels. In the morning her deserted friend discovered only a short note on the dressing table:

'Better, don't you think, if we go our separate ways?'

Marjorie was always hopeful of proceeding through life in
tandem, but it was never her fate to look sweet on the seat of a
bicycle made for two. And this may have helped to sour her temper.
With regard to Dorothy we need look no further than *Olivia* for
a proof of her powerful and impressive responses to love; and I
hope that we shall not have to wait much longer for the publication
of her correspondence with Gide. (By a lucky fluke now preserved
in the Bibliothèque Nationale. I say lucky because Pippa, in a
mood of prudish anxiety for the good name of the family, ordered
Marjorie to burn it; and Marjorie forgot to do so.)

Moral indignation, however, was not an easily observable
feature of the Strachey family. The younger ones were escaping
from that bondage; and though they could blast the institutions
and beliefs of the Victorians, and question the accepted ideas of
their own generation, they usually did so only under pressure, and

half-heartedly. They were much more interested in how people behaved, and were never tired of analysing the defects and virtues of their friends. My mother, on the other hand, supported with excessive zeal all those principles which the Stracheys had long since abandoned; and never troubled herself to examine the personal qualities of her friends. She knew nothing about other people, and cared less. If their views coincided with hers then they were 'nice'. If they deviated, even in the slightest, from that high standard, then they were 'horrid'; and there followed an outburst of a type that, however displaced and ineffectual could still only be described as moral indignation.

I must confess that I have suffered all my life from the same complaint. I can be fired – if a damp squib *can* be fired – even now, by injustice, real or imaginary. I am ashamed of my former propensity to fight the good (or the bad) fight, with all my might; and to become so easily *engagé*. To be involved is to be a partisan and for such the circle of life grows narrower and narrower, until at last one is blinded by one's own myopic vision to a limited view of the truth. No scientist, no artist, should concern himself deeply with the rights or wrongs of mankind if he is to preserve a range of vision superior to that of a mere politician. But for a very long time, far too long, I was a knight in shining armour; and no cause, mine or another's, was so lost that I did not raise my lance to defend it.

At first the strangeness of my new environment at Beaudesert Park kept me fairly quiet; and it was enough for me to learn the customs and manners of the natives. I found nothing to object to in being addressed collectively as rascals and maddening little animals; nor individually as 'you fool' since that term, among ourselves, was so general that it contained no stigma. The game of conkers led to quarrels, of course; but the energy released in striking one of them with another was enough to dissipate the rage of the conquered. It showed us, too, (if we were capable of learning such a lesson) that passive resistance often triumphed over the most active aggression. A conker, violently whirled around at the end of its string and making a notable strike upon that submitted to attack, often split into pieces while the dangler was preserved intact.

One of the reasons, perhaps, why I settled down fairly quickly in my new surroundings was because, in spite of some solid years in Hove, I was inured to sudden changes in environment and the disorders of a broken home. I was capable of adjustment even if I often overdid it. To give the Richardsons their due, I was tenderly treated during all my time with them, and for my first term I was considered as more of a companion to Austen than as a fully initiated member of the school. As far as that goes none of us had any cause to complain. Discipline was mild, authority benevolent; and the school was always run as if it were no more than a larger than usual family. The bigger boys had no power over the smaller ones; and there was no bullying, no beating, no rigid code of manners to make our lives nasty, narrow and unfruitful. We were allowed not merely the freedom to develop along our own lines but positively encouraged to do so. Sir, heedless of our delicate parents, armed only with his instinctive feelings for those of his own age group, amused by our antics and taking a leading part in them himself, preserved us from the strait-jacket of conformity, frustrated (innocently) the more tiresome endeavours of his wife on behalf of the Establishment, and managed to extract from a formless void of primordial matter an order, an understanding, and an appreciation of the richness of life which, if it led to more originality in his pupils than was normal, gave us everything we could be fervently thankful for in later life. I believe my fellows, if any still remain, would support this recognition of his invaluable qualities.

As an individual in charge of small boys he was outstanding; and it may have been his sympathetic interest in our characters and in our active pursuits that made him admirable as a teacher. As coach, crammer, or tutor, he would have failed. He could not bear to stuff us with facts and figures which, he maintained, if rammed down our throats, would have induced a diseased brain as incapable of functioning as the swollen *foie gras* of the wretched and overloaded goose – and far less palatable. He had the supreme gift of the teacher in being able to excite and stimulate the interests of the taught; and he accomplished this without any other resources than those of infinite kindness and patience. I do not say he never admonished us. He frequently did. He could lose his temper with us maddening little animals. But his language was the same as ours, more direct in fact as ours was often sarky and intended to wound; and we rever felt humiliated or out of our depths at *his* boyish wrath. In comparing him with my aunt Marjorie, another born teacher, I preferred his methods to hers. She, too, could stimulate her victims so that they never forgot her lessons. She had a better brain, a profounder knowledge than old Sir; but her instructions were so seasoned with bitter comments and caustic wit that the taught were sometimes deprived, in the loss of their self-respect, of much that was valuable in her teaching; and, so far from being always attracted by and interested in her revelations, were sometimes goaded to respond to them not with their intellects but with their emotions; and the lesson was likely to end in fury or tears. Strangely enough this reaction invariably caused her the greatest surprise; and she never understood the reason for it.

I was slowly introduced, as was Austen, to our future studies. He and I were considered, by his mother, as a unit; and were so constantly together that it could not be long before violence of some sort occurred. While the others went to their labours we were shooed out into the grounds with no positive but many negative instructions. We were not to get dirty, not to get our feet wet, not to jump on the flower beds, not to interfere with Hopkins or his boy, not to hang about the stables, not even to look at, let alone touch Mr Nathan's motor-bike; and so, as there was nothing else to do, we broke all these commandments one after the other. Our criminal activities tended to cement an otherwise uneasy relationship. He was solid and obstinate. I was flighty and inventive. If I proposed an infringement of the law he might in the end agree to it; but only after he had annoyed me with a moral lecture, or even threatened to report me to She-Who-Must-Be-Obeyed. He was the little innocent seduced into bad ways by a hardened sinner; and although it was a connection I refused, indignantly, to recognize, I was at a loss to match an indignation based on moral grounds with one that was only personal. Gunpowder, barrels of it, was to hand. The fuses were laid. It needed but a spark for an almighty explosion. But until I could catch the saint red-handed in some monstrous act that made my disregard for his mother's orders little worse than peccadilloes, I was not in a position to kindle it. But an occasion presented itself all too soon; and I found myself for the first time engaged in defending with vigour and holy wrath the cause of another than myself.

We had been mucking about in the stables where the boy spied us and sneaked to Hopkins. He, shouting, advanced upon us with raised broom; and we retreated behind them to a labyrinth of hot houses, old disused pig-sties, and sheds – one of which Hopkins referred to as the coach-house and the boy, more up to date, as the 'garridge'. It was here that Mr Nathan kept his unruly machine; and as the stables had been occupied by the enemy we decided to

pass the time cleaning and mending our friend's motor-bike in pre-
paration for the afternoon's run. Nuts that were loose had to be
tightened and those that were obviously too tight had to be
loosened. The net result was to leave the 'Indian' in much the
same condition as we had found it; unless, unscrewing the cap of
the tank and judging there was not enough petrol left to get its
owner down the drive, we thoughtfully filled it up with water. Perhaps it was this indigestible mixture that caused all that explosive
spluttering. We had enough sense not to enquire.

As the sound of our tinkering died away we became aware of a
faint tapping accompanied by an occasional squeak. We traced
this to a box trap in the corner which, on investigation, held a little
prisoner vainly trying to escape.

'This'll be fun,' said Austen. 'I'll take it over to that tub and
watch it drown.'

Got him, at last. I instantly blew up.

'You jolly well won't, you rotter! It wouldn't have a chance in
that trap. I'm going to let it go.'

'It's only a mouse, you fool!'

I have just boasted of my generous impulses on behalf of others;
and it is true enough that then, and for much of my life, I was comforted by the thought that I was entirely disinterested in supporting
the oppressed. But I have long since recognized that our noblest
feelings, if traced to their origin, are as selfish as our worst. Purity
of motive is always questionable. Identification with the victim
offers an easy explanation for release of emotions that, on any other
supposition, are not characteristic of the human race. I can admit
that in my battle with Austen, as I had so often been helpless in the
hands of others, and 'only a mouse' myself, some selfish motives
must have stirred in my breast – but I was not conscious of them.
I saw only that a monstrous act of injustice was about to be perpetrated on an innocent and defenceless victim, and that it was my
knightly duty to rescue it from a horrible death. Austen snatched
up the trap, raced outside, and threw it into the nearest water-tub.
I flung myself upon him. As he made contact with the jagged edge
of a spout that served the tub, and rebounded from it, I distinctly
heard the sound of rending cloth. I roared with rage and righteous-
ness, and he with pain and panic. But once he was on his feet again
he got in some good blows and, although his ragged, flapping gar-
ments incommoded him not a little, managed to hold his own until

I pushed him fair and square into a large manure heap which Hopkins had been nursing for weeks. While he was struggling to disengage himself from that rich and unsavoury bog, and sinking ever deeper into it, I had time to run to the tub, plunge head and shoulders into water that was clean if cold, and extract the trap from the bottom of it with its occupant still alive, but only just. I released it near a shed, and with some gentle encouragement from the rear I had the satisfaction of watching the poor little wretch wobble its way to safety.

I'm not going to blame Austen for behaving as nine boys out of ten would have done; and I'm happy to report that he did not sneak, even if it be true that he had no need to do so. His appearance in public, by itself, was more than enough to cause alarm and despondency in his mother; and Miss Whatley reported that all my clothes had to be changed as they were sopping. Sir heard of these domestic troubles during lunch; and tried, as was his wont, to get them into focus, but not to much avail.

'Boys will be boys, my dear. The rascals!'

'It's rather worse than that, Harry. Austen's suit has been torn to ribbons, quite beyond repair as Miss Whatley agrees; and we have had to give him a bath, too.'

'A bath? The ruffian! Whatever for?'

'I'd rather not say, Harry.'

'Oh, indeed! Anything wrong with Dick's suit?'

'Not so much. It can still be worn when it's come out of the airing cupboard.'

'Well, that's something. Did he have to have a bath, too?'

'No. He seemed to be quite – er – fresh.'

'Well, that's something. You mean Austen smelt?'

'That's not the point, Harry, and we really need not go into details. I'm worried about his suit.'

'I should think so! How did you get into such a mess, Austen, my boy?'

'I got pushed into a manure heap.'

'Oh, I see. And how did you get so wet, Dick?'

'Well I had to get it out of the tub, or it would have drowned.'

'I see, I see. Could you tell us *what* would have drowned?'

'A mouse, Sir.'

'A mouse? Yes, of course. There you are, my dear. *Parturiunt montes; nascetur ridiculus mus.* Nothing to make a fuss about. I'll talk to Hopkins who seems to be getting beyond his work. They were only trying to do it for him.'

'Yes, I thought it ought to be drowned.'

'But I didn't. I thought it ought to be saved.'

'So you had a set-to, you rascals! And, my dear, if it hadn't been about a mouse it would have been about something just as silly. Maddening little animals, boys and mice! By the bye, who won?'

'I did.'

'Liar! I did.'

'Splendid, you both won. And what happened to the mouse? Did that win, too?'

'Yes, Sir. I saved it, Sir. It was still quite alive when I got it out.'

'Well, that seems to be the long and short of it, my dear. Simple enough: Righteous Richard saves a mouse.'

There was a happy shout of laughter as those words went round the table. I joined in, feeling very pleased with myself.

'Righteous Richard, save me!'

'Righteous Richard, I'm a mouse, save me!'

'Righteous Richard! Righteous Richard! Righteous Richard!'

'Will you be quiet, boys! Now, do be serious, Harry. What are we to do about Austen's suit?'

'Whatever you please, my dear. Doubtless you will be in correspondence with the boy's mother. That's your business, not mine. And now, for what we have received may the Lord make us truly thankful, Amen.'

'Amen.'

And that is how, o best beloved, I acquired my first nickname.

If the tale of that mouse had stopped there I should have had little reason to complain of my first encounter with the species. Unfortunately, their tales – even those of the house mouse – are inordinately long. The particular is too often lost in the general; while the tail itself so fills the imagination that unless one is very careful, the original and sole cause of all the pother is obscured in a multitude of inconsequential side-effects. So it was in this case, as I have already hinted. Mesdames Richardson and Strachey – how I wish the details of that correspondence had been preserved! – scarcely gave a thought to the mouse. It was Austen's *suit* that worried them: its state of preservation before the disaster, the exact degree of its ruination afterwards, whether made to order or bought off the peg, the quality of the cloth from which it was manufactured; and even a suggestion (raised by Margaret, I regret to say) that for a boy of Austen's age size seven might be a little on the small side, and that he was, most conveniently for *his* mother, in need of another one, size eight. Of course, remarks of this nature only caused the fur to fly the faster, not to speak of a deal of indignation, righteous or not. Anyhow, to cut a long tail short, if I can be so brutal, the parties eventually reached agreement and the costs of the action were reduced to two guineas. Even so, a most expensive mouse.

I am tempted to add that, if not a mathematical mouse as well, it was the cause of mathematics in others. It multiplied correspondence, it added and subtracted to bills; and finally it divided Austen and me into two unequal parts. We went 'our separate ways.' He was retired to the nursery and I was promoted to the schoolroom; and by the time he reappeared among us my other companions absorbed most of my attention.

As a reader I have always been omnivorous. But, to begin with, I was less selective than I am now; and even now if I start a book it has to be a very bad one for me not to persevere to the last word. Nor do I skip. I read, as every reader ought to do, for pleasure and sometimes for instruction. But I have an uneasy feeling that I did not always do so; and I shall try to trace this feeling back to its roots in order to show that a bookworm, such as I became, is made not born, and comes to its food in odd and roundabout ways. Our leisure reading at Beaudesert Park was never supervised. This, like almost everything else about that marvellous school, was sensible and broad-minded; even if authority thought, since we read slowly and uncertainly, incomprehension or boredom would preserve us against any contamination we might pick up from the loose comments of advanced writers. It was felt that of our own accord we would stick to Rider Haggard, Kipling, Conan Doyle, Henty and the science fiction of Jules Verne or Wells. For the most part we did, and it might have worked in my case, too, as I came to read all those authors avidly. Why then, with so much healthy and harmless fodder around me, did I make my first meal of the Bible? Surely, this was indigestible reading, if not positively noxious? And yet I started on it there and then, and read it from beginning to end, ploughing my way through all those 'begats', all those long and unpronounceable names, all those moralities and immoralities, all those miseries and mysteries and other recondite matters I could not possibly have understood, with the greatest satisfaction. No mean feat, though I say it who shouldn't, for a boy of eight. But, for Heaven's sake, why?

It's the sort of problem I relish these days, so I'd better get down to it. It was not for Heaven's sake, as I never had much taste for religious speculation. Nor did I then find the Bible anything like as exciting as *Nada the Lily* or *The Purple Cloud*; and it was only very much later that I came to recognize that the beauty of its language, in the authorized version, was exciting enough to overcome the dullness, the inconsistencies, the barbarity of its matter.

On the surface there were some perfectly natural reasons why I should have set to work on the Bible. Every boy had returned with two or three books of the sort I have mentioned. No one at Tisbury Road in Hove had thought fit to furnish me with similar reading; and, at that age, whatever others do one wants to do oneself. Singularity is dangerous. Luckily for me I *had* been provided with one book, and that one happened to be the Bible. So while the others were marching briskly with Roberts to Kandahar, or with Kitchener to Khartoum, I was wandering for forty years with the Israelites in the deserts of Sinai.

Since we all read what happened to be packed in our playboxes it was quite as reasonable for me to read the Bible as for others to read Henty. I admit there was something competitive in our reading, an unworthy spirit of emulation: the larger, the longer the book, the more status the reader gained; and mine, by universal consent, was a whale among minnows, indisputably a whacker.

On wet Sundays, when we could not go to church in Henley, we held an impromptu service of our own; and as an expert on the Bible I was often called on to read passages from it. On one such occasion I boldly tackled the word 'Babylonians' which I rendered as 'Baby Lions', and brought the house down. At this point, Margery insisted that the Bible, since it contained so much that was indecent and obscene, so much that was morbid and unhealthy, was not proper reading for me; but Harry, who had had a good laugh, replied that, judging from the way I interpreted that holy work, I was not in much danger of being perverted by it. And so, to my great relief, I was allowed to persevere with my nourishing task.

All too soon the last evening of that term was upon us; and for days past I had been chanting, in a chorus with all those other maddening, and ungrateful, little animals in my dormitory, an anthem that most certainly could not be applied to the treatment we had received at Beaudesert Park:

> This time next week where shall we be?
> Not in this Academy!
> No more German, no more French,
> No more bending o'er the bench.
> No more Latin, no more Greek,
> No more cane to make you squeak.
> This time next week where shall we be?
> Not in this Academy!

I don't suppose I reflected on my first evening there. But what a change had come about! Then, utterly lost, I had stood silently, helplessly by the side of my bed, lonely and laughed at until Miss Whatley had come to my rescue. Now I was, as she had predicted, faster at undressing than Simon or David, and neater about folding my clothes than were either of the Horaces. I was accepted as one of the boys, a member of the gang; and I liked my new status so much, and had become so used to it, that Hove no longer sounded to me like home. But the stream of Time was carrying me along with it; and even at Hove things were not as they used to be.

CHAPTER TWO

The most familiar object that met me on my arrival at Hove was Hove itself, though we had moved to a quarter with which I was little acquainted and one that was far grander than the seedy neighbourhood of the Town Hall. This was Margaret's work and part of her great plan, and she consulted no one in its furtherance. She had dispersed most of her household. She had recklessly given up the lease of No. 13, Tisbury Road, and was now temporarily settled – poised for freedom – in a furnished apartment in Lansdowne Place run by a Mr and Mrs Mulholland, a retired butler and his wife. I did not find him sympathetic. Mr Mulholland spent much of his time in a green baize apron polishing silverware, and he detested children. Of the old servants only Prodgers remained as a sort of factotum, looking after us, acting as a buffer between Margaret and the Mulhollands, and doing all the catering. We were in a state of flux. My mother, in spite of misunderstandings and muddles, had reached an amicable agreement with the Richardsons – at least on the subject of their taking in my brother John. So, unimpeded by baggage, she would, at last, be free; free to flirt her way once again to India, to recapture the delicious days of her youth, to dine and dance away the hurrying hours, while some still remained to her, with the uniforms of the Bengal Lancers.

But fortune does not always favour the bold. Margaret had leapt before she looked – and so, it seems, had my father. Her brave bid for liberty had been just a little bit too precipitate. She discovered, to her discomfort, that she was once again in pod. It was still perfectly possible to go to India, but there would hardly be time for more than a waltz before she would have to return. The child

26

must be assured of an English birth; and, at least towards the end of the period, she might find herself a little too top heavy, if not too tired, to whirl all night long in the arms of a *beau lancier*. Without much enthusiasm she, nevertheless, telegraphed the news to my father with the suggestion that she should come out on the next boat. The reply was sensible and negative. Although the prospect was dreary, she was always able to look on the bright side of things. Perhaps her plans might simply have to be postponed; and in the meantime she would not, at any rate, be bogged down by children, servants, or that greatest of all horrors, a home. Ralph would return in May or June; and after the birth of the new child they could all go out together. And so, indomitable as ever, she turned to the matter in hand: the cheapening of Austen's suit with Margery Richardson. She found a use for me in taking that vast correspondence daily, and even twice daily, to various pillar boxes since, as can be imagined, the parties were so eager to state their views that their letters mostly 'crossed' in the post, and subsidiary explanations were required.

I was simply a messenger, quite unaware of the dangerous contents of the messages I delivered to various quarters of Hove, or of the letters I posted. But I was conscious of a vast change in the circumstances of life as I had known it at No. 13. Such attempts at method and regularity as had prevailed in Tisbury Road, feeble though they often were, had given me a feeling of security which had been strongly reinforced at Beaudesert Park. Now the forces of disorder were unleashed. Neither Prodgers nor Margaret had time to supervise our activities, and since if we remained indoors we got in their way, inhibiting Prodgers in her daily battles with Mrs Mulholland and distracting Margaret with loud cries of 'What shall we do, Mummy?' as, pen in hand, she thought up some telling argument in her voluminous correspondence with Mrs Richardson, John and I were usually dismissed as soon after breakfast as was healthy to explore the outside world by ourselves. He reluctantly accompanied me on these fresh wintry walks, not side by side, or hand in hand, but trailing a few paces in the rear. I had to resort to bribery if I was not to lose him altogether. He could post the letters himself at the next pillar box provided he kept up with me – but not all of them at once. That would have released him from my control immediately: the rule was one letter, one box. And the more I had the more sure I was of returning him safe and sound at lunchtime. I resented the responsibility. I found it hard enough to keep myself. Was I also to become my brother's keeper?

It was, nevertheless, from this time onwards that other feelings than those of hostility towards John began to burgeon in me. Our relationship, no longer bolstered by innumerable peacemakers, became more acute and realistic. For much of the day, whether he liked it or not, he had to rely on me; and I, whether I liked it or not, had to see that he came to no harm. As he was in need of this protection I went to great lengths to ensure that he got it; and if Margaret had sent him out without his gloves I would notice it at once, and return to get them, even though he said he didn't want them. On these occasions I felt pleased with myself. But if, as a result of sliding along a frozen gutter, he had fallen over and scraped a knee, I unfortunately felt it was all my fault, and returned cast down to our lodgings. But the mixture of guilt and love was too heavy for me to bear. Authority sat too heavily (and always has done) on my shoulders. I was never one to command and much preferred to be commanded. In charge of John, or of a cricket team, I resorted to bribery and corruption; and never to threats. Besides, it was much more subtle to undermine and topple a leader than to hold such a position oneself by a boring use of force.

I never recaptured the uncomplicated feelings for John which I had at the time of his birth; I was more confused by my relationship with him than anything else. I put it down to malice, or hatred of me, that he persisted in trailing along behind me, tailing me, spying on me, dogging my footsteps instead of accepting what I had to offer and offered sincerely: an equal and friendly companionship in a world that had suddenly become so bleak. I had not consciously thrust myself upon him as leader, and I was wounded by his tactics as well as fearful of them. From the rear he could so easily have tripped me up. But I need not have worried; and I might have reserved for myself the pleasure of posting all those letters. There was a simpler explanation, and one so very simple that it never entered my head. His legs were shorter than mine.

But the solution to this puzzle, and his revenge (if revenge it was), had to wait for more than twenty years. On a walking tour in Brittany, as day after day, starting level, he gradually receded from talking distance, from shouting distance, from sight, I discovered that his legs had become longer than mine. I had plenty of time to remember those earlier walks in Hove, and comforted myself with

the reflection that ignorance of compromise is more excusable in a
child than in an adult. But why should he have accommodated his
pace to mine? Perhaps I was still to blame. '*Dépêche-toi, jeune
homme*', shouted an old hag, '*ton camarade te laisse à la traine.*'
Camarade, indeed! The best part of a kilometre ahead! I don't
suppose anybody has pursued him quite so persistently as I have;
but he has always escaped me. My legs are shorter than his.

The importance of that particular 'hols' was that it marked a
complete break between infancy and boyhood which the mildness
of Beaudesert Park, in spite of novelty and battle, had not immediately achieved. From now onwards I was exposed to the irregular-
ities of life, and while I appreciated the greater liberty they brought
with them I constantly regretted the securities I was used to in our
old home at Tisbury Road. And even when they reappeared in
much their old form, I could not accept them without the deepest
misgivings. In fact I rejected them as temporary and shallow and
put all my hope in the solidity of Beaudesert Park. Wherever we
might spend our holidays, school at least was permanent; and as we
lived there for most of the year it increasingly became for me my
true home. But at this stage, disconcerted by the absence of most of
our old circle, distressed by my mother's uncertain behaviour and
frightened by the Mulhollands, I was without any sort of background into which I could fit. Once upon a time there had been
one. And so, on journeys that took us westwards, with John at my
heels, I often returned to gaze at No. 13 and pausing too long to
stare down at the old kitchen in the hope of seeing Cookie, a new
one with total lack of sympathy and with hard words would issue
forth and drive us away. And so I learnt that the past was dead and
gone, and no happy moment could ever be relived, though the
memory of it in later years might sadly be recaptured. It was a
lesson I read with tears, but it has saved me many more. There is no
reason why today should not be as happy as yesterday, and to-
morrow (except for the one that will mean nothing to us) as happy
as today.

John and I had become outsiders in more senses than one. Toys,
games, and inventive imaginations were frowned upon in the Mulholland era. However, with John's enthusiastic co-operation I
invented a game that looked outwards (and upwards) and involved
the participation of others even if it was only intended to fool
them.

At the time of my birth no one, except Icarus, had got off the ground in a heavier-than-air machine. But in the same year that John was born the Wright brothers, in something that looked quite like an aeroplane, had risen a good two feet above the surface of the earth; and so rapid was progress, or pollution, that Monsieur Blériot had actually hopped across the Channel some years later. Flying machines were still rare enough, however, to be worthy of interest; and the broad pavement in front of the Town Hall, more animated than other parts of Church Road, allowed for the accommodation of a considerable crowd. On this stage we performed. I would point up into the sky and shout excitedly:

'Look, there it goes!'

'Where? I can't see it.'

'Of course you can – just a little to the right of the clock.'

'Do you mean that little speck up there?'

'That's it, about the size of a pin-head. See it?'

By this time we always had a few people gazing upwards and pointing – and naturally seeing it, too. They collected others and the crowd continued to grow even after we had left it behind us. When the weather was cold we were less successful. Any sort of practical joke is evidence of the joker's maladjustment; and in our early years John and I had much to put up with and much to work off. The treatment for this disease did us some good, and the public no harm.

The armistice arranged between Margery and Margaret over the price of Austen's suit amounted to a truce at the end of the holidays; but it is clear to me that the warring parties were deeply suspicious of each other then and for some time to come. The principals did not trust themselves to meet even on the fairly neutral platform of Henley-in-Arden. Our side, led by Prodgers, consisted of two hostages and two playboxes; though I failed to see why John should have one since he was not qualified to rank as a schoolboy, and was destined for the nursery. We arrived safely and without incidents since Prodgers was not the type to attract them even in a train. Margery Richardson, a stickler for protocol, was represented by her old nanny assisted by Barton (Little Bee to his father) and Enid, both junior to Austen. Sealed notes were exchanged with a minimum of fuss – the final reverberations of the conflict – and then

Prodgers retired to the buffet for a nice cup of tea before reporting, round about midnight, to headquarters: a tiresome day for her, but as usual bravely endured. I was looking forward to seeing my friends; and John, though thoughtful and not obviously at ease with his company, was silent and perhaps a little reassured by my presence and high spirits. Miss Whatley greeted me with a warm hug; and by the time I was free to look around John, very much to my relief, had vanished. Proverbially speaking – I admire their concision and authority, but deplore their tendency to contradiction – it would be wrong to say that his absence made my heart grow fonder. It was more, this time, a case of out of sight out of mind. But I react unpredictably to such situations, and it has confirmed my view that a proverb is a shallow thing and not to be relied on. I don't think I brutally abandoned John to his fate. For once I was thinking positive. What a joy that he had become somebody else's business!

One of the great advantages of Beaudesert Park for its paying guests was its restricted size: a small school made a large family. It was small enough for each one of us to receive individual attention and to establish our individuality; and large enough for us, brothers, not to be overwhelmed by the conventional responses required of family life. There were, indeed, many pairs of brothers and cousins among us, but the weight of these holiday relationships slipped from our shoulders as soon as we got back to school. A chum was in far greater demand than a brother, let alone a cousin; and, what was even more relaxing, he could be swopped without the least sense of guilt. We experienced all the pleasures of infidelity and none of its pains; and even relations with our true brothers (though never amounting to chumship) became more natural when we saw they were engaged in the same way and only too glad to escape from the fraternal bond. In that happy land it was never shameful, or dangerous, to be possessed of a brother. If he got into trouble you could be sure his friend, or a potential friend, would come to the rescue. It was only when John, in his turn, arrived at Rugby, that I discovered the sophisticated ingenuity of larger boys could transform any relationship with one's nearest and dearest into a painful liability – a discipline we were never taught at Beaudesert Park. *Floreat, Rugbeia!*

In this winter of my second term, when the grounds were too soggy or frosty for football, or when shivering Authority shirked the duties of a referee, we were sent out on walks, generally under the supervision of Mr Nathan. I believe most of us preferred them to football. So far as I was concerned I must have enjoyed them, as all my life I have been a great walker. Mr Nathan, on the contrary, was a great rider; and if his motor-bike actually got going we were hardly ever able to keep up with it for long. We might, out of decency, plod on for a bit in the direction he had taken; but sooner or later, by mutual consent we would call the hunt off and return to our stables in twos and threes. And if he himself were lucky the Indian got him back in time to escort the last stragglers home. He was more often forced to walk than ride, as Austen and I were by no means the only ones to service his machine.

We waited at the entrance to the Park with the gate open, so that Mr Nathan, once launched by Hopkins, would not lose momentum by having to apply his brakes. Then we followed in his sputtering wake until we reached Willow Walk where we conveniently lost him. This small lane, little more than a bridle-way, made a diversion alongside a stream and led to a farm before looping back to rejoin the main road about a mile further on. It was here that we divided into two parties of cowboys and indians. Each of us was armed with a knife, so that we lost little time in selecting and cutting off suitable switches from the willows. These were to act as levers for the propulsion of pellets. We were too nice simply to throw muck at each other and I suppose it was just possible that the switches might have had a longer range than our arms. But the manufacture and discharge of the bullets was our chief objective. What a pleasure it was to plunge a hand into the oozy banks of that little stream and fashion those neat black sausages out of a stinking bog!

It was the texture of the grenade that required judgement. If too runny it slipped down the stick and fell behind us or on our hands and faces. If too solid it stuck firmly to the tip and failed to get aloft. But a squishy-squashy squeeze produced a projectile that could be attached to the stick and which, as soon as we jerked it at arm's length above our heads, flew off the handle into the enemy ranks in the most satisfactory way. It was never, oddly enough, a question of winning or losing this battle. The greatest good humour prevailed in both parties; and even if, by some fluke (because these discharges were very erratic) a direct hit was scored no one ever lost his temper. Our flinging about of mud was quite arbitrary, and the sole condition was that it should be flung: no matter where, nor at whom. It was as if we were exchanging not the filthiest of missiles intended to befoul our opponents but valuable and highly esteemed tokens of our love for them. We never tired of this game. It was repeated *ad nauseam.*

In the winter season, as the days got longer, as the first snowdrops began to appear, as the buds on the willows swelled, these friendly engagements seemed to reassure us, year after year, that in the springtime of our lives we, too, were subject only to the natural laws of growth and nothing more was expected of us. Our rosy faces, our keen appetites, our happy laughter were manifestations of an inward peace of mind where there was no longer any room for feelings of shame and guilt. During these loving, uninhibited offerings of mud we must have been unloading from within us stores of foul and rotting material compared with which the healthy dirt we accumulated on our outward persons in the process, and which so shocked Miss Whatley on our return to Beaudesert Park, was really nothing to make a fuss about. That sort of muck would always yield to a little soap and water. But what was much more surprising, the graver impurities with which in our lonely infancies we had become contaminated, and of which neither she nor we were conscious, were also being scrubbed away. Not as individuals, but as a group, we had stumbled on a way of eliminating all that filth (or most of it) out of our systems. There is clearly a good case for washing one's dirty linen in public.

It seems to me now that nearly every day of every term held a particular incident of value to me, and more of them were happy than sad. Although my progress was irregular (and during those periods I actually spent with Margaret at Hove or elsewhere, I often had to retrace my steps) it was generally onward, and with increasing confidence, though sometimes at a loss, I accomplished the transitional stage from infancy to childhood without too many difficulties. We do not have to be thrown into the sea to learn to swim, nor to be brutally severed from our families to learn to live. But, on the other hand, we shall never get anywhere if we are only allowed to paddle timidly in the shallows, or if we are held in perpetual captivity by the fatal charms of a mother.

CHAPTER THREE

When the others had departed to take up their onerous duties at home, John and I and another boy called Roby, abandoned by our parents and only peripheral to the family life of the Richardsons, enjoyed all the liberties of ticket-of-leave men with a minimum of supervision. Austen, claimed by Mrs Richardson, returned to prison; and John was released to Roby and me by way of exchange. We three made the best of both worlds. We did not protest at having to eat with the family, and we submitted to going to bed at the usual hour; but that was where our obligations to the Richardsons ended. They were no concern of ours, and it is to their credit that we appeared to be no concern of theirs; or very little. We never mentioned our own families and showed no signs of feeling deprived of them. We were well aware, from observing the behaviour of Austen, Little Bee and Enid, that a family life held too many bonds and penalties to be really tolerable; and we may have remembered from our own experiences how awkward and painful it could so often be. To escape from a family, at any age, is one of the great pleasures life has to offer; and between us we had managed to escape from several. But John and I had reckoned without the reach and grip of the Hovian monster whose protective, prehensile feelers, ever prepared to keep us out of harm's way, so often all but failed to squeeze us to death. For better or for worse the beauty that was a beast could never, never simply let us be.

A tentacle, better employed with the others in caressing the life within, stretched all the way from Hove to the Midlands to encompass the lives without; and a minor discharge of ink from a full sac dismayed and alarmed Margery Richardson into a deplorable activity. Margaret managed to convey to her in many, but not in so many words, that she, Margery, was provincial and behind the times. Did she not realize that every fashionable mouth was now being fitted with a plate? Or, to be strictly accurate, that the mouth of every fashionable child was being so fitted? And would she, therefore, be so kind as to arrange for Dick and John to pay a visit to the best dentist in Warwickshire? Mrs Richardson was horrified to think that, owing to her neglect, her own children might in course of time become long in the tooth and socially unacceptable; and at once determined that an appointment must be made for all of us before any of our teeth had become too fixed in their ways to exclude us from the drawing-rooms of Mayfair, the predestined habitat of their owners.

The first indication we had that anything was up was when, on a week-day, we were ordered to rise in our best suits; and the next when the larger of the two Henley taxis (known as the Hearse on account of its speed) arrived to collect us. And it was not until we were *en route* that we were informed of the ordeal before us – a wise precaution since there would undoubtedly have been delaying protests. As it was we were held in check only by firm reminders not to rumple Enid's frock, and to try to behave like gentlemen. What with Austen's new suit and his sister's starched frills I found my movements very restricted. Little John, who realized something of what went on at the dentist's, and Little Bee who did not but suspected the worst, became tearful; and Austen looked far from comfortable. Margery, in sole command of the party, was busy and abrupt; and the only member of the party more or less at ease was Roby who, also dressed in his best, accompanied us merely out of a sense of decency. After much discussion between the harassed Richardsons it had been decided that, without any instructions from his parents, it would be wiser to let his teeth fend for themselves.

I was the first to enter the chamber of horrors after my plea that, in times of stress, the convenience of ladies (with a glance at Enid) should always be considered before those of gentlemen, had been turned down. I had scarcely got into the seat before, with the usual battle-cry of 'Open wide, please', he crammed a far too hot ball of what looked like plasticine into my mouth and pressed it home. That impression is as vivid now as it was then; and I remember wondering, as he scooped it out again, whether he was going to remove all my teeth at the same time; a mass extraction that would have saved a lot of trouble in the future, and incidentally would have made the manufacture of a plate quite superfluous. But, though clogged with bits of stuff that tasted like rubber, my teeth and I returned to the waiting-room in one piece; and to Roby's tactless enquiry of what it was like, I maliciously replied, 'Awful.' The others thought so, too; but our sufferings were as nothing to those of Little John. In him the dentist discovered a patient really worthy of his hire. It seemed that his teeth were exceptionally prognathous and, most interestingly, not all to the same degree; so that something in the nature of a fortress would have to be built with crenelated walls, half-moons, and here and there a flying buttress to prevent the defenders from flying away altogether. However, by the time the dentist had finished with him the prospect of a party in foreign surroundings did much to raise even his spirits. But only Mrs Richardson herself, and Roby, did full justice to that sumptuous spread. The day was cold but we could not manage such hot morsels as buttered tea-cakes or crumpets, and had to confine our attentions to chocolate éclairs and orangeade; and even these failed altogether to remove from our tortured palates the taste and texture of indiarubber and clay.

In most memoirs dealing with the author's early days shocking stories are told of the interception, scrutiny and censorship by the school authorities of both incoming and outgoing mail. They naturally fear that the children in their care will circulate reports to their parents which, in extreme instances, might lead to a loss of income. A bout of ordinary homesickness, exaggerated beyond measure and normally forgotten as soon as written by the victim, might end in the removal of the child or at best in a tiresome correspondence with an outraged parent. The excuse under which this denial of privacy was exercised was always the same: merely a matter of seeing that the handwriting was legible while the real object of the examination, the letter's content, was never mentioned. The Richardsons passed this test pretty well on the whole, and if Margery was a little too curious as to the identity of our correspondents she was always ready to inform our world at breakfast that her Aunt Agnes was thinking of spending the summer in Salzburg; or that Granny Richardson was knitting a pair of socks for Austen. It was Margery who insisted that the post was not to be left in the hall, where we could find it for ourselves, on the grounds that we might pinch each other's letters. So she had the pleasure of examining the handwriting on the envelopes she distributed.

Towards the end of those hols a registered parcel arrived for her which, as usual, she examined carefully before opening it.

'Now what can this be? From Warwick, of all places! I've ordered nothing from Warwick since Austen's new suit. Must be for you, Harry! Golf balls, perhaps?'

But Sir, it seemed, got his supplies from Dunlop's in Birmingham.

On opening the parcel a formidable array of hardware spilled out onto the table, each item carefully labelled; and, strange though it may seem, we scrambled quite eagerly for what we fancied might be our property – though there was a natural reluctance to claim the most imposing of these artifacts. The five plates were named but in such a manner that it took some ingenuity to find out for whom each was intended (except, of course, the stupendous fortification which Vauban himself might have envied, and which was clearly destined for Little John, even though a neat tag attached to a portcullis indicated that it was for Enid Strachey). In fact there were three plates for the Stracheys, and the other two were for Dick and John Richardson. However, amidst much hilarity, by a process of elimination and experiment, by passing plates around from mouth to mouth, and especially because the four remaining objects were so light and trivial that it hardly mattered if a perfect fit was not at once agreed, we managed to sort them out in the end; and thus accoutred we were prepared to greet our defenceless comrades and the new term armed, so to speak, to the teeth.

But epics such as these are always blessed or cursed with a coda that rumbles on and sometimes fiercely returns on its tracks like the distant mutterings of a thunderstorm that, just as one hopes the worst is over, suddenly increase in volume and notify us that its repercussions have by no means come to an end. The Iliad was happily followed by the Odyssey, Paradise Lost unfortunately had to be Regained, and tales about teeth must recur until we escape from the dentist's chair equipped with a pair of falsies which we hopefully believe may put us out of his reach for ever.

Some guffaws from Arthur Harry showed that he was now fully aware that there was more entertainment to be extracted from our end of the table than from the leading article in *The Times*. Physically and mentally vigorous, genial, cheerful and downright with us youth, he was always happy to see us in good spirits and seemed, on the surface at least, to be always happy himself. But this exuberance concealed an inner timidity and malaise, a fear of any situation that could not be resolved by commonsense, and a social ineptitude that almost amounted to a phobia. He brought comfort to those in no need of it, but his boisterous words only plunged the disconsolate into further depths of gloom. I give him credit for genuine sympathy with the distressed yet the shock tactics he employed were not calculated to bring them much relief. If he saw a boy in obvious trouble he was so much disturbed that he could think of nothing better than to laugh him out of his misery with the stock phrase: 'What on earth's the matter with the ruffian? Looks like a dying duck in a thunderstorm.' I suppose he could think of nothing more miserable than such a creature in such a situation; and hoped to infer that, at least by comparison, the object of his kindly intentions had by no means reached so hopeless a state as that of the wretched bird. It never had the desired effect. So vivid was this picture that it served only to convince the boy that, if anything, his case was worse than ever.

It was not remarkable, then, that catching sight of Roby, who seemed to find nothing amusing in our activities, and whose face had got steadily longer and longer, Harry should have drawn attention to his plight with the usual comforting comment; and the usual result. Reliable old Roby – he was at least ten – made no reply but burst into tears, and Margery with an arm round his shoulders led him from the room. On her return, alone, Harry was curious to know what all the fuss was about.

'Nothing serious, my dear. He'll be all right in a minute. He just felt a little out of things. As soon as I told him I'd ask his mother he began to cheer up. After all, it does seem a bit unfair. Why shouldn't he have a plate like the others?'

I welcomed the summer term *con brio*, and Miss Whatley – it was my turn to greet her – with a hug. We got off to a good start with the usual announcement of a whole holiday. It was to be a picnic in the Wood.

We set off in fine style. The first to depart was our outrider, Mr Nathan; his duty to see the way clear for the more ponderous vehicles in the cavalcade, and formally to take over the wood and hold it until our arrival. Then the gardener's brother, known to us as Hopkins the Hearse, loaded with urns, hampers, the house-keeper and another old trustie, let in his clutch and lurched down the drive in the wake of an Indian rejoicing in a new set of piston rings and obviously out to break all speed records. Hopkins the Garden got the loudest cheer when he drove up to the front door with two fat horses in need of exercise towing the wagonette behind them. The boy looked a bit glum on the box as he had hoped to go in front with the younger Hopkins; though he was envied by the the rest of us as we sat facing each other in two long rows.

We assembled in a clearing near the entrance to the wood.

'All present?' asked Harry, confidently.

'No, Sir. Mr Nathan's got lost.'

'Who saw him last?'

'I saw him in the village, Sir.'

'We all saw him in the village, Sir.'

'Not in any difficulties, I hope?'

'No Sir, just punctured. Usually takes him half an hour to mend them.'

'Well, when he does turn up, Margery, ask him to patrol the river – just in case. I shall keep a general look-out elsewhere. And when you hear three blasts on this whistle, you maddening little animals, come back here at once.'

We charged off into the wood, following the river down-stream as far as the waterfall and the pool. Above the fall two rocks, close together, formed a natural arch open at both ends, and it did not take us long to block up one entrance. We began to collect wood for a fire, but in the midst of our labours three shrill whistles interrupted us. From the beginning to the end of life I never seemed to have enough time to do all the things I wanted to do. Whistles from the outer world, shrill, insistent, were perpetually calling me back to reality from the land of dreams and wonders where I lived so un-profitably and so happily. But a picnic lunch was not to be despised and offered a reasonable alternative to the immediate pleasure of furnishing a cave. Besides, I could return and complete the job afterwards.

The two old bustling bodies had done their work splendidly. We fell into three groups and were catered for accordingly. The grown-ups were served with cold roast duck, a bowl of Russian salad, biscuits and cheese, and a Dundee cake, while Sir produced a bottle of wine for their refreshment. We boys plundered the hampers and helped ourselves to a variety of delicacies from sausage rolls, hard boiled eggs, buttered rolls, ham sandwiches, a round Dutch cheese, lettuce, tomatoes, down to a large tin of mixed biscuits; and even then we were allowed a bar of chocolate each and a choice of drinks: stone jars of ginger beer or bottles of American ice-cream sodas. The Hopkins brothers, too delicate to expose themselves to the fresh spring air, had retired into the smoky security of the Hearse where they regaled themselves on thick sandwiches (crusts left on) of roast beef, ham, egg and cheese followed by an apple turn-over and washed down by a generous supply of bottled beer. The two old dears picked and chose where they might, but for them was reserved a large thermos of strong sweet tea. And of course our old Hopkins had not forgotten them two 'osses. They stood in the shade tossing up their nose-bags, very contented. And what of the boy? He had collected what he fancied from the various dishes, together with (perhaps unwisely) a bottle of beer, and now lay stretched on the ground under the wagonette in blissful slumber. I assisted at twelve of these feasts (there was always another at the end of the summer term, known as the Pool picnic, when the main business of the day was to bathe) so I could hardly be mistaken in the menus. Arthur Harry forgot to say grace either before or after the meal. Perhaps there was something about the forest of Arden which would anyhow have made it inappropriate. But he was always happy to see others happy, and in the middle of the feast, watching us tuck in silently, remarked: 'How's life, you rascals; as you like it?'

'Yes, Sir, thank you, Sir. Three cheers for Mishter 'nd Mishes Richerson. Hip hip hooray! Hip hip hooray! Hip hip hooray!'

We were excused the usual rest after lunch and again dispersed into the wood. My morning comrades deserted me. I was alone, just as I had hoped, and made straight for the cave above the water-fall, a cave that was now to be my home in the wild, wild wood. I provisioned it with a slice of cake, a bar of chocolate and a bottle of American ice-cream soda. I adorned it with bluebells; and a few rare primroses. More sticks I gathered and set to work rubbing them together so that a precious spark might give me a fire. I could not get so much as a wisp of smoke to encourage me, and began to wonder whether it might not save time to borrow a box of matches from one of the Hopkinses. But that would have been laborious and also cheating. So I simply pretended I was warming myself by a fire which was already lit and fell to (as if that lunch had not been enough for me) on the haunch of venison, the wild fruits and the mead, the spoils of a successful day's hunting. And then – no wonder – I fell asleep, lulled by familiar shouts from the rest of the tribe, echoing from every corner of the wood. Safely and soundly I slept. But I woke with a start.

The happy reassuring cries of my fellows had ceased. All was quiet and the wood itself now seemed to be sleeping in the warmth of the afternoon sun; but not as fast asleep as it should have been. I heard strange little rustlings among the dead leaves: a dry stick snapped near by; a breeze had sprung up and the branches of the trees began to creak; and the regular splash of the waterfall seemed suddenly louder than before. Could I hear, or was I meant not to hear, the feeble cries of Horrie drowning in the pool? And while I was wondering if I dared to look I was startled by a sound I had never heard before: a sort of whining, coughing bark, plaintive and high pitched – perhaps a demon of the wood whose rightful kingdom I had invaded. Nearer and nearer it sounded as I crouched in my cave frozen as stiff as a field-mouse in the moment of danger. Not to be seen – that was all I could hope for. But I was discovered and for a moment we stared at each other. I saw a narrow, furry brown face with large pointed ears, and a mouth that snarled or perhaps laughed, showing its teeth. Then in a flash it had gone; but I was still all alone in a wood that seemed to be wilder than before, and larger, and gloomier; and when the thought came to me that the others had left me behind and that I would have to spend the night there, I leapt to my feet and, without a glance at the pool, rushed away in the general direction of the clearing. And now to my joy three blasts on a whistle shattered that eerie silence and was answered on all sides by the comfortable, raucous sounds of my lost companions, sounds of which I knew the meaning. The wood seemed to be alive with them which had, so short a time before, been alive with others far removed from my safe and ordinary world; and then I became aware of mysterious unseen forces which surrounded me and which I might never be able to understand however long I lived.

'What's the hurry, Dick?'

'I saw a reddy brown face with pointed ears, Sir.'

'A fox, by Jove! Scared you, eh?'

'Yes, Sir.'

'Well, I'm not surprised. If anyone tells you the great God Pan is dead, don't you believe it.'

'Peter Pan, Sir?'

'No, my boy, that's rubbish. Pan, one of the Greek gods. We shall be doing some of them this term; and I'll tell you about him then. I only wish he'd chased the others out, too.'

They came straggling back in twos and threes, fearless, and under their own steam. Nothing, obviously, had happened to any of them – nothing like what had happened to me. But the last two to appear had met with physical disaster, as Sir quickly noticed. Mr Nathan and Horrie seemed to have been exposed to the full force of a monsoon and arrived hand in hand, soaked to the skin.

'Good heavens, Nathan! What on earth – you look like a couple of – ahem – whatever happened?'

'Oh nothing. The lad slipped in. Fished him out. A bit wet.'

Miss Whatley cast an admiring glance at the hero.

'Aren't you going to thank Mr Nathan for saving your life, Horrie?'

'No. He didn't save it.'

'And that's true enough. More mud than water. Think I'll get along and change.'

Horrie was wrapped up in a rug and sent off in the car with Miss Whatley.

This summer, besides Greek gods, Latin constructions, and best of all, cricket, we had a Coronation on our agenda. In the normal way it would not have affected us; but for John and me there was a mystery connected with it that I have never been able to solve with certainty. A few days before June 22nd 1911 an urgent dispatch from Margaret required our presence at Hove – and this in the middle of the term! We were met at Brighton station by our father who drove us in his brand new Ford to Mr Mulholland's – quite a thrill that ride as he was always a little too casual in his steering. But we got there safely, and were happy to see old Mumbo-Jumbo from whom we had been parted for so long. Prodgers was still in attendance. We were never given any explanation for this unexpected trip; and all I can do is to make a guess. The day after the Coronation we returned to Beaudesert and on the 29th of June Ursula was born. Could Margaret, that fearless creature, have considered the possibility of a disaster? Did she want to have a last look at us, or did she want us to have a last memory of her, in case anything went wrong? She struck me as looking exactly the same as ever, in the best of health and spirits, and eager for amusement. I find it hard to believe that we had been sent for merely to partake in the celebrations at Hove which, of course, were memorable. Was our loyalty to the new king to be imprinted on our minds by this extravaganza? After all, the bonfire we had all been building at Beaudesert would have had the same effect.

But the fact that, as a spectator, I assisted at the Hove celebrations is very real to me. The jingo spirit was at its height in England, revealed at Hove during the daylight hours of Coronation Day by much waving of Union Jacks; and enormously increased after dark by the injudicious consumption (to make us merry) of, in the words of the old song, whisky, beer, and sherry. That evening I went to bed at the same time as John, and even managed to get to sleep though I was a member of a conspiracy from which he was to be excluded. At ten o'clock my father and mother, in full evening dress (how did she manage hers?), woke me up and led me on tiptoe, wrapped in a blanket, to a waiting taxi. We joined the procession of cars along the King's Road between the two piers, there and back and there and back to the music of military bands and the wild cheers of excited crowds on the Prom. Bonfires burnt on the beach by the fish market, rockets rising from the ends of the piers exploded in galaxies of falling stars, and set-pieces of red, white and blue flares floated on the calm but smoky sea. The piers themselves were brilliantly illuminated with fairy lights. I have never forgotten the excitement of that night and its startling beauty, though I suppose if I'm to be accurate I must admit some of its fascination for me was undoubtedly due to its being an experience shared with grown-ups, and not suitable for young children like John. I boasted of this experience on our return to Beaudesert; but when they pointed out to me the ashes of the enormous bonfire we had all been building near the rookery, I felt instantly that I had been deprived of a treat that really mattered. The lucky devils had been allowed to set fire to their own work, and, what's more, had been issued with squibs! How much more thrilling to have chucked one at a friend than merely to have watched passively as fire balloons brooded over the waters and rockets rose above them into the dark blue skies!

CHAPTER FOUR

Alys Pearsall Smith was our Auntie Lou. Her brother Logan had a certain literary fame, enough to ensure him of at least one biography, and he wrote his own life, too. As I only met him once when I was a child, and our dislike for each other was instantaneous, I need say no more of him. Auntie Lou's sister married the famous connoisseur and collector Bernard Berenson; while she herself had, four or five years before I was born, married Bertie Russell. When I first became acquainted with her that marriage had long since foundered and she had become a convenient depository for unwanted Strachey children. She was, of course, no true aunt or great-aunt to any of us but we owe her adoption into the family to Oliver. On the 31st of May, 1911, he married *en seconde noces* Rachel Costelloe (Aunt Ray) and Auntie Lou happened to be Ray's aunt; and so she became our aunt, too, since who's going to bother to distinguish between aunts of one generation and aunts of another?

Before I give an account of the summer holidays our cousin Julia, John and I spent with Auntie Lou at Ford Place, near Arundel, I can't resist telling an anecdote of her nuptial travels with Bertie in China. Examining the bill after a night in Shanghai they were amazed to find that their expenses had been reckoned as for a single person. The earnest couple, unwilling to cheat the management, questioned the bill, and were told that it was perfectly in order. 'You see, sir, we make no charge for concubines.' I have never come across this little story reported elsewhere, and I have completely forgotten how I got hold of it. Part of its humour for me now is that I still can't imagine any one less like a concubine than

Auntie Lou. When I saw her in the flesh I examined her, of course, from the wrong point of view, with the critical and innocent eye of a child, and found her merely intimidating. But, I suppose, to a heathen Chinee, those luscious amazonian proportions, that authoritative disposition, and the possibility at any moment of the infliction of deliciously brutal punishment, might have excited feelings of lust. With orientals you never can tell.

For my earliest encounter with Julia I have had recourse, probably for the last time, to my mother's little red notebook. There I find that, on the fateful visit to Scarborough which was to give me a brother, 'we stopped at York for one night so that he might meet his cousin, Julia.' There is probably more in this than the importance of a social engagement between a girl of four and a boy of three, but it must remain unexplained. Perhaps, even then, Julia and I had time to hit it off – words too prophetic of our later relationship. For many years I was no match for her malicious wit, an example of which may be found in her charming novella *Cheerful Weather for the Wedding* where John and I, harmless clowns, were mercilessly ridiculed. I have never resented it since the scenes in which we appeared were so brilliantly executed that I collapse with laughter on every reading.

Before we heard of these holiday plans, however, Mrs Richardson announced to the school at breakfast that Dick and John had acquired a little sister – an event that held, obviously, far more interest for her than for us. I remember at first being anxious as to how my fellows would react, fearing, rightly, much ridicule. But they were silenced when Mrs Richardson enquired how many of them had sisters; and it turned out that quite a lot of them had, so we were not alone in our shame. Later on, I asked what she was called and was told that her name appeared to be Urcula but that it was not distinctly written. I suppressed this name as it sounded too queer to be accepted without facetious comment; and a few days afterwards I was relieved to read it as Ursula. Margaret's spelling was always inspired but perhaps, on this occasion, so soon after the birth of her daughter, her hand may have trembled. Ursula's other name, however, was boldly written and clearly decipherable: Margaret. We were not to see little Ums for many moons, and by that time she looked quite like a human being. As I had commented unfavourably on John's arrival so he, in his turn, showed his disappointment, more reasonably perhaps, on Ursula's.

He was reported to have said to Mrs Richardson: 'Bother! It should have been a boy, then it could have joined Dick's army. It ought to be sent back.' I can't remember at that, or any other time, having an army; but if then I had one it clearly consisted of two general officers, and an addition of a private to the strength must have provided some relief to one of them.

On arrival at Ford Place we were greeted by Julia and Auntie Lou, strangers to us but amiable; far less formidable than the rambling old farmhouse in which we were to spend the summer. Originally Tudor it had, at various periods, been pulled about and added to, so that it was something of a jumble of many styles. The tall, ungainly brick chimneys, so typically Sussex, in spite of enormous hoods seemed to release as much smoke into the sitting-rooms as ever escaped by the normal vents; and it is a fact that the old Sussex builders never mastered the complicated system of up and down draughts of air; or perhaps they favoured the delicious smell, even if accompanied by the eye-pricking side-effects, of wood smoke in their parlours. The ceilings were low and darkly beamed with oak; the corridors, narrow and winding, were of the kind that squeaked under foot during the hours of daylight and creaked of their own accord at night, and which then too often gave rise to sinister thoughts at a time when one would have preferred to be without them. Beneath the roof vast, shadowy attics invited exploration – if anybody dared to. For lighting we did not exactly rely on the variable strength of the moon, but candles, even if there had been enough of them, were a poor, if exciting substitute for electricity; and there never were enough of them. John's and mine, on our way to bed, was constantly a-shiver and sometimes, naturally or unnaturally, was blown out. If that old house was not haunted by ghosts then it ought to have been; and I, who had recently become an addict of such fearful tales as *The Hound of the Baskervilles* and *Ghost Stories of an Antiquary*, was soon convinced that it was overpopulated with visitants from the other world. I passed these notions on to John in the hope that he would be able to reassure me; but he so instantly agreed with me that my fears, and his, were simply redoubled. We shared a room together, which was something; but even so united, we felt we would be no match for any ghost worthy of the name. How we envied Julia who shared a room with Auntie Lou! She clearly would stand no nonsense from ghosts. But us they could visit with impunity.

To begin with we had to get used to the strange accent and phraseology of our new protectress. Auntie Lou, a liberal-minded Quakeress (and Shakeress, though not in a religious sense) from New England could never address us, except in the plural, as 'you'. Thees and thous, wouldsts and shouldsts, and other curious and unnatural tongue-twisters had to be translated into English before we could make out what she was saying; and her nasal intonations, wherever she had picked them up, bore no resemblance to the short and sturdy vowels of the Sussex dialect. She spoke her language, all three of us spoke ours; and although neither was modified communication was hardly ever brought to a halt between the parties. Her rule was on the whole benign even if she a little favoured Julia. After all she knew Julia from of old and, stout feminist as she was, seemed to think that John and I were ceaselessly plotting to degrade, humiliate, and get the better of our delicate little cousin. And we may find some excuses for her since we know that her experiences of the adult male had not been particularly happy. But it was one thing to have been in charge of Bertie and quite another to be in charge of two small boys; and I don't think she ever appreciated the difference. Days would pass during which John and I were free, as we never had been before, to do anything we liked; and then, suddenly, for a very minor misdemeanour we would receive a solemn and high-minded lecture. She, at times, felt that we were in need of culture so that she encouraged the reading of poems, the acting of plays and charades, painting and music, and even scientific instruction; and at other times, apparently forgetting that we were under the same roof with her, we were returned to the wild accompanied by Julia. Irregularity was the order of the day. Never once did she mention going to the lavatory after breakfast, and only on rare occasions were we made to have a bath.

This lack of interest in bodily hygiene was more than compensated for by a devotion to purity of mind – an exact reversal of those disciplines so early instilled into me by Margaret and old Nanny. We may sympathize with Auntie Lou's carefree attitude to the daily and punctual evacuation of the bowels when we take into account Bertie's anal preoccupations, and the number of times she must have been forced to listen to philosophical and mathematical disquisitions on that interesting subject. She would have thought it more simple to put an end to windy argument and let the matter drop; which, in its own good time, it usually did. Similarly, a bath was just as boring, nothing more than a slothful luxury, and only needed when the body had become an offence to delicate nostrils: a reluctant concession to the fastidious demands of an effete society. Nor was it at all inconsistent that, almost as soon as we had arrived, she announced in significant tones that the three of us were to have a bath together; since for her it was the togetherness that mattered and not the bath. She would have plumped for the bathroom as the venue for a biological enquiry on the grounds that it was more seemly and less shocking to childish ignorance than a more contrived parade in the drawing-room; where, indeed, the keenest observations might have been obscured by billowing clouds of smoke. The facts of life were to be revealed to the three of us as normal and natural. At the very beginning of our association, before we had had time to make our own discoveries, which she believed might turn to mockery and lewdness, she would do her best to scotch that ugly snake on the head, and show us that the human body, whether male or female, was among the most beautiful of God's works and to be respected and reverenced as such.

It is much to Auntie Lou's credit that in an age when children were kept in ignorance of such matters and were hypocritically supposed to take no interest in them, she made so honest and straightforward an attempt to instruct us in the mysteries of sex.

'John, thou wilt put away thy battleship.'

'Why?'

'Thy cousin is going to have a bath with thee tonight.'

'I don't mind, Auntie Lou, as long as she doesn't sink it.'

'Chuck it out, you fool. There won't be room for her otherwise.'

'Now Julia, dost thou notice anything different from thyself in thy two cousins?'

'Yes, they've got something odd between their legs. Looks like a pink slug crawling over two pink potatoes. Does it hurt them, Auntie Lou?'

'And dost thou see anything about thy cousin, Dick?'

'No, nothing, Auntie Lou. How did she manage to lose her thingy?'

'And thou, John, though at thy age it can't mean much to thee?'

'It means as much to me as it does to Dick. I don't see how, as she hasn't got a little thingy, she can pee? Do you?'

'And now as you all know the difference between boys and girls it will be time for thee to get out of the bath, Julia.'

'But I hav'n't even soaped myself yet.'

Here ended the first lesson, and the last we were to receive from
Auntie Lou. Not much progress, apart from the visual, was made
and I have an idea that our instructress suddenly lost her nerve and,
under heavy fire from her pupils with questions not always to the
point, brought the session to a hasty end. After she and Julia had
departed John and I relieved the solemnity of the occasion by a
bout of horseplay during which I sank the battleship, was pushed
over by him and ended up with a chipped tooth. But, though all
of us were a little worse off owing to Auntie Lou's initiative, some
of us in our persons and property, others in their self-respect,
enough curiosity was engendered to keep the three of us busy for the
next few days during which we were left entirely to our own
devices.

In these early confrontations little girls have a decided advantage
over little boys: at least there is something available on which to
comment. On a similar occasion, though not stage-managed by
adults, Simonette was privileged to get a close-up of her cousin
Percy and remarked that it was just like a tea-pot. Julia's descrip-
tion was elaborate and a little too picturesque, perhaps for the
benefit of Auntie Lou; and shows more than a trace of early malice
so far as we were concerned. Simonette's on the other hand, owed
nothing to any high-minded entrepreneuse since, during a game of
hide-and-seek in the woods, she chanced on the boy in the act of
spouting, and it strikes me as being more accurate and just as vivid.
I must say I wish I had more examples to offer; but if I began now
to make a collection of these early feminine pronouncements on the
male organ I might run some hazard of the law. In families which
lack brothers and sisters of approximately the same age it is notice-
able what an important part in these discoveries is played by
cousins; who, in my experience, are never so useful again.

A certain curiosity, if nothing else, had been raised in our minds
by Auntie Lou's unfinished symphony in the bath; and we were
certainly not slow to pursue our own sexual enquiries under the
bridge that spanned the old canal at the bottom of the garden. I
confess I was not particularly moved or much interested in the
anatomical differences between Julia and myself. It seemed to be
totally unimportant and even rather boring; and I was far from
feeling that a mystery had been brought out into the light of day,

and made plain. Nothing of those delicious febrile unsatisfied
desires that had haunted my infancy remained in my mind and
Julia's charming little body failed to resurrect them. She lifted her
skirts so that John could see for himself that she was perfectly
capable of peeing, even though she had to squat down to do it and
was denied the pleasure of direction. Not to be outdone by this
performance we, of course, showed her how we did it, and pointed
out that we had the advantage of a greater range. She agreed that
this was entertaining but that she was far quicker. We must have
felt a little guilty all the same in spite of Auntie Lou's permissive
attitude; and so we agreed that these experiments, if we had
occasion to refer to them among ourselves in grown-up company,
had better be concealed in a code. To pee, therefore, was 'to queen';
to shit was 'to king'. Until these operations lost their first appeal
we gathered every morning in the canal, kinged and queened in
company, and judged each other's contributions with a fervour
that would have delighted old Nanny and Bertie Russell. I think
John and I must have queened it over Julia just too much for her
patience, because she challeneged us to a queening match the next
time Auntie Lou gave a garden party. In full view of the guests we
were all to pee on the lawn, and the winner would be he or she who
was not detected. Like the sporting fools we were we did not consider the odds and agreed to her terms without a thought. When
the fatal day came Julia innocently sat down on the grass and
rose almost at once with a smile of triumph to watch John and me
rolling about on our tummies and struggling with our fly-buttons.
These contortions were remarked on by the spectators. We were
told to stand up and were horribly exposed. Ashamed and dripping,
we were driven into the house to change our trousers. After this
distressing scene John and I came to the conclusion that there was
more to a girl, or anyway to a girl like Julia, than was readily visible
in a bath.

   Julia's interests did not always coincide with ours. I think that
Auntie Lou may have considered us a little rough, and our games
either too childish, too masculine, or too barbaric to permit so
delicate a little doll always to be exposed to our vicious behaviour.
She need not have worried, as Julia was perfectly able to look after
herself; and, being the eldest, generally took the lead in our
adventures as in our discussions. On the subject of marriage, for
instance, we had to defer to her choice since we had reached a

stage where the polygamous dreams of infancy had given way to the realities of monogamy. It was in vain that I pleaded primogeniture. She was going to marry John, and that was that; but the preference had no effect on my relations with either of them, and whether she was absent or present there was as little discord as ever between us brothers. While Julia was engaged with the piano, John and I were busy with the water game. Each chose his drain-pipe and waited expectantly beside it with anything capable of holding water. The spout from the kitchen sink was generally the most profitable, but on very rare occasions (and if one had been cunning enough to get inside information) the drain from the bathroom yielded larger dividends and to collect them all required an array of treacle tins, jam jars, and even pails which, filled to the brim, magnificently overwhelmed the owner of a ginger beer bottle mingily holding a mixture of potato peelings and soap suds. Auntie Lou never understood why John and I were so keen on her having a morning bath. One or other of us would, so long as that game was popular, burst into the room she shared with Julia and beg her to have one. Once, to my dismay, to my horror, dashing in unto her, I found her completely naked, and before dashing out again had time to see that poor Auntie Lou had suffered much the same fate as Julia. It was with awe that I reported some additional discoveries to John; who frankly did not believe them.

'I say, Julia isn't the only one who hasn't got them!'

'How do you mean?'

'Well, Auntie Lou hasn't got any either, She's got a bit of fur though, which Julia hasn't got.'

'Fur? Git out!'

'I said fur. I suppose you know what fur is?'

'Of course I do. Bears have it. Do you mean to say that underneath she's a polar bear?'

'No, her's was a sort of dark patch just there and nowhere else.'

'More like a brown bear, then?'

'Like a brown bear that had shaved itself all over and forgotten that part.'

'How awful! Is she a bear in disguise, do you think?'

'Couldn't tell you. Might be. But that's not all.'

'She can't have anything else the matter with her?'

'Well, she has. Where you and I and Julia have chests she's got two great balloons.'

'Git out! Has she really? Oh, what absolute rot! If she's got these balloons why hav'n't we seen her rise into the sky?'

'She may float about at night, for all I know. Anyhow, if you don't believe me, go in quietly one morning and see for youself.'

'No thanks, never again. It's just one of your stories, you fool, and you needn't think you've frightened me.'

'I didn't mean to. I thought you'd like to know, that's all. Shall we have a go at our submarines today?'

The second half of the holiday at Ford Place was by no means so placid as the first; though, all things considered, still enjoyable and interesting. Auntie Lou's sudden concern, towards the end of the holidays, for manners, health, and group activities, none of which in our view needed attention, bored us and led to trouble all round.

The Stracheys could not be called *bons viveurs*. They ate to live, though on occasions they could tuck in to what they fancied with as much relish as the rest of us. Almost everything disagreed with Lytton whom Carrington for years had to coddle with a variety of milk sops. James, more worldly, made a pretence of high living and indeed enjoyed a steak when Alix wasn't looking his way. But he, too, was a connoisseur of rice puddings; and when we were house-keeping for the two of them at No. 41 Gordon Square he nearly drove Simonette mad with his instructions as to the proportions of milk to rice, how long the mixture should be cooked, and the exact degree of brownness required for the skin. In my youth I remember a sad scene at No. 51 where I often shared the mid-day meal with Lady S., then in extreme old age. A dish of raspberries had been placed before her and she greedily attacked them. After a few mouthfuls she flung down her spoon with a cry of despair: 'Can't manage the pips any longer. What's the point of it all, Dick? Sans teeth, sans eyes, sans taste, sans everything. Curse it, how I *loved* raspberries!' Poor old Grannie! and I only laughed as I patted her hand. Marjorie specialized in pears; but the only other fruits all of them enjoyed, if they can be properly called fruits, were *marrons glacés*. Between them they must have got through at least a couple of cwts a year. They one and all were suspicious of vegetables but could sustain life on soup. My father and Pippa were fond of curries, a taste they had acquired in India; and so was Oliver. He was remarkable in being positively nauseated by both fruit and vegetables and no one had ever known him to eat either. I shared with my mother a more catholic taste and came to enjoy most sorts of food set before me. But in this respect John took after his father's family, especially after Oliver; with whom, besides an abhorrence of vegetables, he had much in common and who was the only one of them he really liked. John was to suffer martyrdom for the sake of these Strachey genes which, in other ways, could not be described as dominant. Food preferences may change or become fixed as with other characteristics, and can in themselves reveal much of the personalities of individuals.

But I must return to my muttons, or rather to John's greens. The vegetable in question was a cabbage, and as everybody knows they vary according to age and the ability of the cook. The mutton and the potatoes, at this famous meal, just passed muster; but even Julia and I commented unfavourably on the soggy, apparently uncooked and tasteless cabbage. John said nothing but refused to eat it. Auntie Lou, now seriously concerned with metabolism and health, insisted on his eating it. Silently, he put his knife and fork together, showing us that, according to the rules of etiquette, he had finished.

'Very well, John, thou shalt sit there until thou has eaten thy greens.' As there was no reply to this ultimatum Auntie Lou left the room in a rage. Julia and I lingered on in the hope of persuading the delinquent to come to terms with authority; but neither of us was prepared to eat the remains of that cabbage for him which would have been the simplest solution to the problem.

'Wouldst thee eateth thou cabbage, John, I wilt let thou ride my donkey all the afternoon,' said Julia.

'Yes, you idiot; and I'd lend you my best submarine. Why, there's not more than four, say five mouthfuls, well, possibly six; and then you'd be free to come out with us.'

He did not take the trouble to reply. He disdained our friendly carrots, laid his ears back, dug himself in and prepared for a time-less struggle with Auntie Lou. Julia and I had no joy in that afternoon, constantly abandoning our games to come and see how much remained of the cabbage. It was always intact; though it got steadily less inviting as the hours passed. So, too, did John. He consumed not a fibre of it but, face to face with that poisonous plant, he had assimilated one of its properties: its colour. When, at last, we all came in to tea, he and the cabbage were still sitting it out.

Auntie Lou, a softie at heart and more of a fool than a tyrant, had the sense to realize she was beaten, capitulated without conditions, and ordered the offensive vegetable to be removed. John celebrated his victory, quietly; contenting himself with an enormous tea, thus proving that he could eat more than most people when he wanted to. But this episode rather unsettled us all and divided Ford Place into two distinct parties. We three began to be less open with Auntie Lou since we discovered she could bite.

She, for her part, balanced uneasily between the liberal views of Bertie and the fundamental responses of the New England puritan, swung disconcertingly from laxness to severity. Julia and I thought of her as, on the whole, not a bad old thing; but John hated her. She began to segregate us from Julia who was burdened with the piano, dancing classes, and even sessions of sewing; and she took to spying on our outside activities. Waiting for waste waters was forbidden and our collection of tins destroyed.

One afternoon, giving vent to a natural, if generally concealed, vein of exhibitionism, Auntie Lou invited the village to an entertainment at Ford Place. Julia was to open the proceedings with the piece she had so long practised on the piano. This was to be followed by a recitation of a poem entitled 'That Little Boy in Breeches', with many opportunities for clowning, by a well-known comedian; and finally we were to return to the serious with an outstanding delivery of 'Jabberwocky' by Auntie Lou. She had suggested to John that he might care to sing a nursery rhyme but, on his firm refusal, having learnt her lesson, she did not press the point. For some days we studied our parts and ranting actors begged to be heard from morning till night and one of them so persistently rehearsed his lines that, in the event, he proved to have become quite wordlessly perfect and had to leave the verses wholly to the prompter. The applause for Julia's performance was loud and sustained; and it may have unsettled me as I stood in the wings. But, on seeing all those benevolent faces as I marched on to the stage, I was at once struck dumb with fright; and after what seemed several years of silence the audience had to put up with whispered lines from the prompter which I listened to with the same patience as they did. However, at the end of each verse, I loudly shouted the chorus:

> That little boy, that little boy,
> That little boy in breeches,
> He takes the cake
> And no mistake,
> That little boy in breeches.

At the end of that last chorus, I did, at least, remember to take the cake that stood on a table, and rushed from the platform accompanied by an uninhibited roar – of laughter. Success, success; but at what a cost to pride! And the cake did not taste too good, salted by my tears.

But, at that age, I did not linger long in dark corners or brood on the sorrows that flesh is heir to, though later on I was not able to be so mercurial. Sustained by the cake, perhaps, and curious as to the next item on the programme I crept into the back row of the stalls, and was well rewarded by the spectacle that met my eyes. Auntie Lou strode on to the stage fully equipped for the hunting field. She did not, of course, confine herself to the part of a parent rejoicing in the prowess of his son. That would not have given her genius enough scope to show itself in all its variety. She was the Jabberwock, the Jubjub bird, the frumious Bandersnatch, the son, the father, and even the Tumtum tree where, as the hero, she stood awhile (rather as I had done) in uffish thought. We were made to see how mimsy were the borogoves in that tulgey wood as (transformed instantly into the Jabberwock) she whiffled through it, and burbled as she came! Then once more the hero, slashing wildly with the whip, she conquered the monster and very modestly (though shaking the stage with her weight) went galumphing back to be her own reception committee.

> 'And hast thou slain the Jabberwock?
> Come to my arms, my beamish boy!
> O frabjous day! Callooh! Callay!'
> He chortled in his joy.

And then after this *Te Deum* of praise, this paean of triumph, which set the crockery ringing, she dramatically lowered her voice to a dying fall:

> Twas brillig, and the slithy toves
> Did gyre and gimble in the wabe:
> All mimsy were the borogoves,
> And the mome raths outgrabe.

For a space the audience, stunned by the artist, purged as never before, remained silent; and then showed their appreciation of this amazing performance with a wild outburst of cheering and stamping of feet. I like to think how civilized those Sussex villagers were, contrasted with the barbarians of today who, at the end of every musical composition, drown the last few bars with their unwelcome applause. Of course, Auntie Lou did not plumb the profounder deeps of this great surrealist poem; and can easily be excused since the author himself must have remained ignorant of its unconscious significance. Nevertheless, even on a purely representational level, she led us into regions hitherto unexplored, and allowed us a glimpse of those marvellous and magnificent vistas open to a poet's view. My love of poetry, with its source flowing freely from my infancy, was not diminished by my own wretched fiasco; but it may well have been reinforced as a result of witnessing this noble interpretation of the beautiful obscurities of Carroll. I owe more than a cock to Auntie Lou.

In the beginning there was fear. To be capable of experiencing it is so valuable a concomitant of life that without it we, and many other species, would long since have become extinct. As with a species, so with individuals: the fearless meet an early death, the coward lives to fight another day. But if a cautious approach to real dangers is admirable, it is futile to give way to the imagination and invent others not detectable by our five senses. It needs all our ingenuity to escape intact from those we meet with every day in the world we know. It ought to keep us too busy to waste time and thought on how to avoid perils from worlds which are only discernible to those unlucky individuals cursed with a sixth sense. In my early years, assisted by ignorance and credulity, I was subject to extrasensory perception, to sudden panics, to a belief in ghosts and ghouls, demons and witches, werewolves and vampires, to the gruesome spectacle of a chinaman imitating, nightly, the last phase of a famous Cheshire cat, and to a generalized fear of the dark. Nor did I get much comfort from the thought that God and his angels might preserve me from the Devil and his; since both parties, if I put a foot wrong, would not hesitate to consign me to everlasting fire. The inexplicable existed for me and unmanned me; and I was much more afraid of fabulous horrors that would destroy me if I dared to walk the earth at midnight than the scarcely considered dangers of a gay promenade at midday, jumping from sleeper to sleeper, along the tracks of the LB & SCR. But unlike many children, whose irrational fears survived to haunt and throw them off balance in later years, I was lucky enough to escape that fate.

By the middle of September the blue skies had begun to take on the darker tints of lead. Little sudden winds arose and stirred the calm reaches of the rifes; and though the sun still shone with all its former glory the air we breathed seemed stale and oppressive. The year required a change of season, and all of us a change of scene. We had had enough of the summer and more than enough of each other. Our lethargy was only stirred by little sudden winds of irritation; and as I sweated away the long, uncool nights, my thoughts roamed heavily along the creaking passages of the old house in tune as ever with the elements now in the pangs of labour. I had not lessened the sombre suspense of those nights by reading again *The Hound of the Baskervilles* – not the best of bedside books for the imaginative child.

We had begun to react to the emotional excitements which had culminated in the frustrations and triumphs of our recent performance before the villagers; and our tensions, tediously increased by those of the weather, could only be released by storm. Late one afternoon a mass of black cloud built up over the marshes around Pagham harbour, and for once the light of the sun was obscured before it set. A sou'wester blew the tempest along towards us and the first few drops of rain were falling as we went to bed. Our candle guttered, of course, in the passages, and finally went out as we reached our room; but there was still enough light to take off our clothes and get into bed. There we lay expecting the worst while vivid sheet lightning all too clearly revealed and obscured the lurking monsters around us. A thunderstorm might have been some relief since it would have drowned the lesser noises which were so much more mysterious and unaccountable. This time, however, we were favoured with a monsoon. The fitful pitter-patter on the roof increased steadily in volume and changed its rhythm from that of a stately minuet to a wild gallop, interrupted now and again by a flurry of rain hurled against our windows. I did not dare to ask John whether he heard anything particularly unusual since by giving voice to a fear it too often becomes real. Perhaps it was just as well that I remained silent because, as I was about to speak, a sound unutterably fearful, at first a little muted by distance and seeming to come from far away, in every lull in the storm sounded louder in my ears. I was not to be put off by any thoughts of booming bitterns or noisy marshes. No, this was the baying of hounds in full cry, and the chorus rose as the pack neared their helpless quarry. I heard the pattering of their feet, not on the roof-tops but along our corridor; and now their voices stilled as they panted and sniffed and scratched at our door.

'Dogs,' screamed John, thus proving that he had been in telepathic communication with me all the time. That was enough to set me off, too. We outbayed the pack and finally aroused Auntie Lou from her slumbers. She lit our candle for us and thoughtfully took us out into the passage which we could see for ourselves was empty.

'Just a nightmare, boys. You can keep your candles lighted; and remember I'm only next door if you need me.'

We got off to sleep at last, but even so I was woken once or twice again during that terrible night by the Hounds of the Stracheys.

There is a sequel to the dreadful events of that night which I shall not conceal from the amateurs of the ghost story. As, in the beginning of our era, miracles and magical manifestations abounded and, later, in direct proportion to the advance of science and the retreat of human credulity, were rarely recorded; so in my own life, my infancy and boyhood were decidedly richer in supernatural revelations than my later years. Long afterwards, in a conversation with Ray – a hard-headed woman of business and, as such, an ideal mate for Oliver – we were discussing ancient times and, in particular, the never-to-be-forgotten holidays at Ford Place. She knew the house well, and indeed it was there that I first met her. She had heard all about that ghostly pack and gave me some further information which I'm glad I did not pick up at the time. A previous owner of Ford Place had built an extensive range of kennels, and had won many prizes at Crufts with his breed of greyhounds. One night a disastrous fire had swept through the kennels and all the hounds had been burnt to death in the flames.

These experiences, I think, may have rattled Auntie Lou; and she must have sent for help, because shortly afterwards Ray appeared on the scene to deal with the preparations for our departure once again for Beaudesert Park. But before I leave Auntie Lou I can gratefully record that *two* candles were provided for us during the remainder of our time at Ford. There was a sensible matter of factness about Ray that quickly dispelled any grisly recollections of our unwelcome visitors. She was direct and spontaneous in her approach to us, and seemed to know the language of boys and what would appeal to them better than any other woman I had met with up to that time. Puffing away at a briar, striding along the banks of the Arun in knee breeches, discussing football, cricket and hidden treasure, she successfully diverted our thoughts from the coming encounter with a dentist in Arundel. So that woeful anticipation was reduced to a minimum; and I entered the familiar torture chamber with hardly a tremor. We got off scot-free. In John's case the dentist was so overwhelmed by what he saw that he quite forgot to look at what might be lurking underneath the fortifications. He would not presume to meddle with what his Warwickshire colleague had prescribed. With me he went to the other extreme, found nothing the matter with my teeth, and was unwise enough to comment that a plate, even so simple a structure as mine, was quite superfluous. On the way home Ray, no doubt relieved that everything had gone off so quietly, offered half-crown prizes if we could chuck a stone to the other side of the Arun. I won this money easily, and John won his for an effort that fell only a little short. But I fancy I might have forfeited the reward if Ray, engaged with John, had noticed the particular object which followed the stone and was hurried away on the ebb to the rich grounds of Bognor. There, full fathom five it probably still lies since neither fish nor fisherman would find any more use for it than had I.

CHAPTER FIVE

After the overwhelming events of the last few days at Ford, and burdened by a sameness which I never had the patience to endure, my spirits rose rapidly with my return to Beaudesert Park. They were not dampened by the defection of Gerald from our ranks, who, while driving a tunnel through an enormous castle on the beach, during the holidays, was buried in tons of sand.

It must not be thought that I was indifferent to his death. It has taken me many long years to comprehend the grim finality of death. That particular reality I have only just, more or less, come to accept; and I have always shirked facing up to it, in spite of a recent, very clear indication, in my own case. I do not, of course, believe that my friends have taken up residence in another world, nor that I myself would meet them there in due course, rather as one might hope to visit them if they had chosen to live in foreign parts. No, the dead are as much with me now as when they were alive. I do not come across them as I do, from time to time, old friends and enemies whom I have not seen for years; but in exactly the same way that I greet these figures from the past and renew ancient conversations and feelings where they had broken off, so I fully expect to welcome the dead walking along Gower Street, sunning themselves in Gordon Square Gardens, or prawning on a spring tide among the rocks of Peppercombe. It can be of no satisfaction to them, I am ready to admit; but, in my way, I, too, am faithful unto death. The next time I see Gerald we will build an enormous sand castle, and we shall happily forget to make a tunnel.

My attitude to the dead of all species, old departed objects, even to past events that can never be repeated unless in the pages of this

book, although often unrealistic, and one which the strong-minded
will denounce as a weakness, has nevertheless sustained me during
the gloomiest passages of my life and procured for others a longer
one, in my memory, than that ordained for them by nature. I
simply cannot bear to think of their bones mouldering in the grave,
of their ashes scattered ruthlessly by the winds or, worse still, confined in funerary urns from which they cannot escape. Nor am I
comforted by the optimistic view that their souls, and mine, will go
marching on. I would believe this if I could, willingly; but, until a
surgeon produces the article in question during a post-mortem, I
shall remain a sceptic. And besides, it's the body with all its un-
doubted impurities and fallibilities that I would wish to see in
action, not a tenuous wraith purged of its humanity and fit for
nothing but the boredom of eternal repose in Abraham's bosom. I
must confess that I have never seen even the bodies of the dead so
far; yet, since once dead there's no more dying then, may I not be
allowed to think of them as just round the corner? In my turn, since
I can sometimes bring myself to face the abominable reality, and if
I absolve those few who have loved me from any concern with the
wanderings of that mythical *animula vagula, blandula* of mine, is it
too much to ask of them that they should spare a thought to my
corpus, the vile body by which they knew me? May I not take a sort
of comfort, should she survive me, that in the sweet remembrance of
one of them my life will be prolonged? I can agree that this is a
selfish dream; but not that it is more foolish or without foundation
than the visions with which all of us, from the beginnings of time,
have sought to overcome the dreariness of death.

Death itself is merely the last step we take in life, and is nothing
to worry about; though the way in which we are to die engenders
the most fearful thoughts even while we are in the full flush of life.
If we are lucky enough to escape its physical pains, and simply fall
into an endless sleep, the last few final days must always be filled for
us with the special sadness which overwhelms those about to depart
on the longest journey; and for which, no matter how powerful our
delusions, there is no cure. Our loved ones have come to see us off at
the station but, once we have chuffed away, they can tear up their
timetable, since the train on which they might expect us to return
is not indicated. Sadder still, for all the love they have given us,
which is our life itself, we have repaid them with the grossest of
infidelities – our death; and so, mingled with our sorrow, we can

only take with us to the green and grassy grave a sense of insufferable guilt. Could we not have loved them more, could we not, somehow or other, have lived forever?

To return to a more cheerful prospect: before leaving Ray, I had deliberately saddled myself with a burden compared with which my reading of the Bible in a year was as nothing. We were both to blame but, I think, she much more so than I. As an adult she must have realized that such an undertaking, had I persevered in it, would have had a deleterious effect on my work and very possibly on my health; and if she had calculated that I would soon give it up as hopeless, she had reckoned without the pertinacity of one with the blood of the Severses in his veins. For my part, it was partly greed and partly an over-optimistic assessment of the sheer magnitude of the task; and I am prepared to admit that it was I who first broached the subject. I had so easily won that half-crown from my sporting aunt that, in an unlucky moment, I decided on another feat that would be just as easy – merely a question of time – and for which the reward would be even grander. Merely a question of time, indeed! I was still engaged on it when I went to Rugby, and the ten shillings I received on its eventual fulfilment were undoubtedly the least profitable I ever earned in my financial career. If the prize were contemptible, might not the labour have been so, too? Am I to go down to history as literally (one might almost say, figuratively) the only human being who has ever counted up to a million?

The school year that now began was as delightful as ever, and varied little from my first. I was expanding in all directions and my interests became correspondingly sophisticated. The practical Ray had shown me that money had to be earned. It was a new idea and one that I was prepared to explore; though I have long since discovered that unearned money is much to be preferred. Even in those days tips were far more profitable than the wretched weekly pocket-money doled out to us at school and for which we may be said to have worked. Half a sovereign that my father, when he was in evidence, slipped out of the little case that dangled on his watch-chain; two half-crowns from Pippa as I passed through London; and a florin from Margaret on the platform of Henley-in-Arden, was wealth indeed compared with the three pennies we received on Sunday mornings. Moreover, only *one* of those could we spend as we wished. The other two were devoted to charity, or were sup-

posed to be, since it was hazardous to drop a fly-button into the
verger's purse as it travelled from hand to hand along the pew,
especially if Sir was on duty that week; and fatal to 'forget' to insert
a penny in our respective Dr Barnardo's collecting boxes since, if
fourteen were not found there when they were emptied at the end
of term, the difference had to be made good and bankruptcies were
not recognized. It was just possible to deprive the vicar of his tithes,
but out of the question to play the same trick on the waifs and
strays. So, at the very best, we were left with two pennies that we
might call our own; and the loss of the important button, multiplied by twenty on occasion, was a source of mystification and
annoyance to Miss Whatley on Monday mornings.

During the winter term of 1912, we enjoyed a prolonged period
of bright, frosty weather; and discovered another use for the pond
than as a happy hunting ground for tadpoles. At first its ripples
were stilled by a thin coating of ice under which pockets of air
formed into complicated whorls and sometimes, under pressure, the
ice shuddered and there was a loud report. But after a few nights of
temperatures well below freezing the ice thickened and darkened;
and one sunny morning, after Sir had cautiously ventured over the
middle of it to the other side, it was declared safe. The greater part
of the pond was reserved for the skaters – Sir, Margery and Jimmy
(who always had everything) in any case were the only ones who
had skates – and the rest of us, at that point where the pond forced
the drive to take an S-bend, shallow and a little impeded by iron
reeds, were confined to a slide. The Richardsons, with Jimmy in
their wake, amazed us with their graceful evolutions. They waltzed
arm in arm to the music of a hiss, flew from end to end of the pond,
turned in the tiniest of circles, and chalked up delicate figures-of-
eight on the frozen blackboard; and to do all that, balanced on
nothing more substantial than a knife-blade of steel, seemed to us
miraculous. We found it quite a business to keep upright on our
solid feet and more often than not reached the further bank backwards and on our bottoms. Jimmy, always inclined to show off, and
given to ambition, sometimes kept us in countenance by ending up
the same way. But, on the ice at least, firmly supported by one or
other of his partners, his swanky improvisations were so controlled
as neither to embarrass nor destroy them in a common ruin. There,
when he fell, he fell alone. And I must not forget the chewing of
icicles, the crunch of which in our mouths was more to our satisfac-

tion than the taste; nor how Fabian and I liberated twigs within our reach by sucking away at the glassy walls behind which they were visibly imprisoned. He and I snapped off bundles of silvery grass from the larger tussocks and threw down their spears on the bone-hard drive where they tinkled as they fell and flashed like tiny rainbows in the rays of a cold bright sun.

The seasons were, to our impatience, capriciously irregular. It seemed that nothing could ever hope to penetrate, in either direction, the rocky ground. A little later than usual, however, the magic worked. Soft airs and heavy rains set the world to work; and almost before we knew what had happened those of us a little instructed in the odes could appreciate the beauty of the verse and its triumphant harmony when the Roman poet concisely declared: *Solvitur acris hiems.*

In the earlier days of the summer we played a game that in Sir's opinion was far less healthy than cricket. Under the elms in the rookery bands of Red Indians and cowboys engaged in battle; and prisoners were tied to the trees patiently (and pleasurably) awaiting death after the most refined and exquisite tortures. I was just as happy to be the victim as the executioner, and ignorant of any of the deeper implications that might be seeking expression in the aftermath of these encounters. But one day, when the bell sounded after the morning break, the cowboys had been in too much of a hurry to release the Red Indians, and Sir found half his pupils missing. He was directed to the rookery where he discovered to his horror that almost every tree held a bound and sometimes gagged prisoner of war. Among the first was I, but still articulate, and I protested it was only a game. In his opinion it was a rotten game, and as he went from elm to elm on his errand of mercy the rookery resounded to his cries of rage and above all, of disgust. We were sorry we had upset him so much but never understood why he was making such a fuss about nothing; and, perhaps, he did not understand it himself. But he might have *felt* that so direct an interest in the pleasures of receiving and inflicting punishment could only be wrong and, if it could not be entirely eradicated from the maddening little human animal, would at least be better employed, worked out of the system, or, at the very least, decently concealed on the cricket pitch. And so it was for the rest of that summer term.

Dick, John and their father

Dick, John, Ursula and their mother

John and Dick

Sir's intensive coaching may have been innocent, or it may have been revenge for the nasty shock we had given him. It was not too difficult, for the enthusiastic, to make the first (and only) eleven; and I shall not be boasting when I say that I received my colours in due course. There was not much competition. Some were rejected as too small, some as too weak, some because their bespectacled eyes failed to focus the ball, some as potential examinees; so that anyone not actually numbered among the halt, the blind or the lame, might reasonably hope to get a place in the eleven.

I believe that when Sir picked up the gauntlet thrown down by the headmaster of Donnington Hall, and accepted the challenge of a match on foreign territory, he was suffering from a severe bout of euphoria. He had recently played a nice little innings for Warwickshire against Sussex at Edgbaston; but it did not follow, stretch the laws of homoeopathic magic as we may, that the batsmen of the Park would do likewise against the bowlers of the Hall – nor does it seem realistically to have entered his head that a school, run on the same lines as a public school and with over eighty boys to choose from, was likely to fall before one that had less than thirty and those, to a man, a rabble rout of *francs-tireurs* deprived of the discipline and spirit of the military machine. We might have given their fourth eleven a game; but their first?

It was tremendously exciting to drive all that way, nearly as far as Tamworth, in the dear old Hearse, encouraged by Hopkins whose deeds on the village green, if true, should have assured him a place in England's side against Australia; but the selectors preferred younger men such as Woolley, Hobbs and Rhodes – and they were probably right to do so. I think Hopkins was too excitable to have restrained himself to the getting of those last few runs in singles. It would have been all or nothing with him; and the Aussies would have walked away with the Ashes. As a supporter of ours he kept our spirits up until we arrived on the ground. Then, the sight of the great stone prison in which our hosts were held captive; the immense size of the ground; the flags flying from the tents; a crowd of spectators; a boundary line clearly marked in whitewash (no long grass for them); a pitch as level as a billiard table; stumps all of the same size and colour awaiting only the bails (a refinement we were not accustomed to); the pavilion into which we were ushered, fitted with so many modern conveniences which our old walnut tree lacked; the enormous youth whose grin, as he approached Bobby our captain, and shook his hand, seemed less friendly than derisive; then, I say, all this unfamiliar ceremony and grandeur sent our spirits sinking. Nor did the spectacle of Sir, spotlessly robed in a long white nightdress, conferring with the other headmaster similarly attired, do much to raise them. If Sir was to be an umpire he could hardly mean to play on our side; and that left us with old Froggie Lévis. We would have swopped them about willingly since if Sir was a better player, Froggie, in spite of his knowledge of the finer points of the game, was so devoted to us that he would un-doubtedly have made a better umpire.

Bobby lost the toss and the giant chose to bat: a slight relief for most of us; and there was further encouragement as, issuing from our shelter to a polite round of applause, we discussed a tragic history that, in the wonderful way such stories soon become known to all, had reached even our ears. Their opening bat had that very day been told that his mother had died. The headmaster, either callous or surprisingly understanding, saw no reason why he should not play. The youth was to carry on as if nothing out of the ordinary had happened to him. Our team, as a whole, did not see it in that light. It felt confident that such a disaster was bound to unnerve him; that Fate would grant us at least one wicket, and that an early one; which in turn could have an unsettling effect on the rest of the side, and against all odds, result in our triumph. I, however, was not at all cheered by the information that had encouraged the others since I instantly put myself in the boy's place, and wondered what on earth I should feel like if anything so awful were to happen to poor old Mumbo-Jumbo. So far from showing a brave face to the world I would have run off into the deepest recesses of the rookery, and have hidden myself there from its cruel realities, where none but blackie-tops would have heard my cries of despair. At long-stop, hardly ever employed, I had too much time for such miserable reflections; and when, as a result of a fine leg glance, the ball came near enough for me to have stopped it, I awoke with a start but failed to reach it as it crossed the boundary. How deeply involved is man with his mother be she alive or dead! His and mine, between them, had added another four runs to the total.

But the death of *his* mother, to our astonishment, had the most lively effect on his play. Never, we heard afterwards, had he shone so brilliantly. He was said to have been, always, a good opener; a

sound and steady bat, but on the slow side – a prop for those to
come. Now, he did not even wait to get his eye in but in the very first
over slammed George three times to the boundary and Max met
with the same punishment. All our bowlers were treated with utter
contempt, and most of us bowled. If he had not become careless
he might have carried his bat. At last Jimmy brought about his
downfall. The bereaved boy was offered a harmless half-volley and
decided to lift it over the bowler's head and out of the ground. But
Jimmy leapt into the air and caught it one handed at full stretch
over his head. A stentorian voice from the refreshment tent made
itself heard above the roar of applause: 'Well caught, boy! Up the
Park!' We were decent enough, relieved enough perhaps, to clap
their hero all the way back to the pavilion. The scoreboard read:
77 for 1, last player 67. And now, stalking towards us, a tiger with
an appetite for lambs, came their captain – the grin still there, but
undisguisedly carnivorous. For the few overs only which Fate (and
his headmaster) allowed him, he ceased not from slaughtering us.
If, by chance, he failed to score he would swagger down the pitch
and prod it. Before each ball he would stare round the boundary
until he felt sure he held the crowd's attention, and then, with a
twirl of the bat and that infernal smile on his face, take guard.
Pride, however, goes before a fall. When a good-length ball from
Jimmy, at which he had slashed but missed by miles, was taken
neatly by Horace behind the stumps, naturally enough we all loudly
appealed for a catch at the wicket. To our unconcealed joy and
the tiger's utter amazement his headmaster raised the fatal finger.
It was, of course, a moral judgement and, as such, deserved in my
opinion; but the reproachful look he gave the Head, as he passed
him on his way to the Pavilion, and the malicious nod he received
in return, were indications that, so far as the laws of cricket were
concerned, he was not out. Their headmaster could comfortably
afford to administer this little lesson in courtesy. The score now
read 119 for 2, last player 24 (all in boundaries). One more wicket
fell to Jimmy with my assistance. I caught a dolly in the slips, and
felt it made up a bit for going to sleep at long-stop. At tea, they
declared (reluctantly, but on advice they could not disregard) with
the total 143 for 3.

The tea was far too good for either side to fraternize; and the
conversation was limited to essentials. 'Pass the buns, Thomson
Ma.' 'Leave a *few* sandwiches for the rest of us, Roby.' Neither

team would have shone in a Mayfair drawing-room; but both were
able to interest the spectators, though in different ways, on the field
of play. We, for our part, lost wickets with almost the same speed
as they had made runs; and when I joined Bobby, who had
remained intact from the beginning, the score read 9 runs for 5
wickets, last man (Horace) 0. His cousin George had made the same
score, and I expected to follow suit. It was a demon bowler, as fiery
as his red hair, who had petrified us, though it was a steadier com-
rade who had taken the wickets. 'Try to get out of his way, Dick,
and you'll be all right. He doesn't often get them straight.' This
was good advice, I dodged nimbly about between square leg and
point and survived an over in which the demon failed to make
contact with me, my bat, or the stumps. Off the last ball of the next
over, Bobby got a run to my great relief, and I watched him treat
that brute for once, and once only, as he deserved. The first was a
long hop and Bobby pulled it over the midwicket boundary; and
Sir, astonished, had the satisfaction of raising his hands above his
head to signal a six. Unfortunately, our one and only supporter,
hopelessly confused by this time, with a roar of 'Shoot, Villa,
shoot!' encouraged Bobby to score another goal. He tried to do so,
indeed, but missed a full pitch which shattered his stumps. 16 for
6, last man 14. During the time it took Froggie to come in their
headmaster had had a word or two with the long-suffering captain
of Donnington Hall, and Froggie received, with all the *sang froid*
for which his countrymen are noted, four slow and harmless
deliveries. The other bowler was also changed; and the new one,
though subtle, was of the slow variety and unlikely to cause much
physical damage.

Their tactics resulted in a stand; and although the score
remained as it was neither batsman had to retreat. And our play,
which in these unchivalrous days would have merited the slow
hand-clap, was greeted with respectful silence. I was always one
for getting on with life and became restless when inactive. At last
I could bear it no longer. I hit out and snicked a ball through the
slips which was worth two runs – a bad stroke but welcomed with
applause by the crowd. I suppose this bit of luck must have gone to
my head. I played the same stroke again to the next ball, but
correctly this time; and it ran gently along the ground in the
direction of a distant third man: an easy run, perhaps two if we
took the first one smartly; so without waiting to hear from my

partner (it was his call, of course) I galloped off down the pitch. But
Froggie, either annoyed at my initiative, or scenting danger where
there was none, and relapsing under pressure into his native tongue,
sternly ordered me back: '*Idiot! A ta crise!*' Back I scampered to
the shelter of my crease. By this time the crowd, excited by the possibility of a run-out, were offering all sorts of wild advice which quite
unsettled Froggie. I was horrified to see him advancing towards
me, shouting as he came: '*Viens, donc, puisque tu le veux, mais
vite, vite!*' So once again I charged down the pitch.

In the meantime the English – an excitable race at bottom – had
been fumbling about with the ball; so much so that there was still a
fair chance of getting that run. But Froggie and I, meeting half-way
down the pitch, became involved in an elaborate dance of death,
quite unable to pass each other to safety. There Lévis and Strachey
were stranded. (And Strachey, I am now reminded, not for the first
or last time: as witness so many telegrams dispatched from foreign
parts ending, after a plea for money, with the words, Stranded
Strachey.) But by now the keeper, who had been hysterically per-
forming a *pas seul*, eventually removed the bails. But which of us
was out? The umpires consulted. Theirs simply shrugged his
shoulders. We were so inextricably entwined that, technically speaking, *both* of us were out. But that was impossible. Froggie now inter-
vened and, as an expert, put forward a solution that astonished the
other two umpires. Neither of us was out, he claimed. 'How so, you
maddening – ?' 'I don't think you were watching the wicket-keeper,
Sir. He removed the bails *before* he had the ball in his hands.' This,
besides being a brilliant lesson in umpiring, might well have been
the case. But Arthur Harry was not to be outdone in generosity by
his colleague; and he, too, now and then, was capable of a moral
judgement. It had *not* been my call. 'On your way, Dick.'

Val had slogged about a bit so that the innings closed with our
score at 31. After the final ceremonies – three hearty cheers for
Beaudesert Park and three less enthusiastic ones for Donnington
Hall – we bundled into the old car, congratulated by a jovial
Hopkins. 'Might a done wuss – a lot wuss!' I don't remember how
Sir got to the ground; but he certainly returned with us, probably
with a view to raising our spirits and lowering those of Hopkins.
But the men of Warwickshire can hold their drink, and apart from
being ordered to reduce speed from a reckless fifteen miles per hour
to the normal ten, communication ended there. The odd thing was

that we did not need any comforting remarks from Sir. We were in
splendid form; and it was not just relief that the ordeal was over.
We had been hopelessly beaten, but we had proved ourselves to be
a side, a team, a band of brothers; and we had become aware of an
identity that, for once, seemed to be more satisfactory than that of
the lone individual. Not every man's hand was against us. Our
own were not; and surely other people might well, considering the
odds, have felt that we 'might a done a lot wuss.' We found something kindly to say to each other all the way back, and were resolved
that one day victory would be ours.

Back in the schoolroom, Ancient History, full of marvellous stories,
legends of men and gods, prehistoric monsters and much odder
ones only existing in the fertile imaginations of our ancestors, was
one of my favourite lessons. I never attained to Greek, much to my
regret, and have been forced to rely on translation. In that department Harry could only take on a few of the brightest among us,
those in whom he discovered the possibility of a future academic
career, or the immediate prize of a scholarship. But the rest of us
were kept well informed on that and kindred subjects. Although
he was a practising christian he found no difficulty in accepting
both the ancient and modern versions of Genesis. If anything he
preferred the modern since it allowed more scope for entertaining
variations. We were sometimes led to believe that monstrous forms
of life had for timeless ages, inhabited the earth before man
appeared. At others, that a mere week, if that, separated the fully
fashioned from one another. We were not at all surprised to think
that while fearsome reptiles encumbered the open spaces we, in the
unlikely shape of tiny lemurs, were confined to the trees where we
had to pass our time for millions and millions of years until there
was room enough for us to descend to the ground. By easy stages we
were told of the evolution of the species, of the evolution of man:
lemurs, monkeys, anthropoid apes, tool-makers, savages, barbarians, Greeks. Very special the Greeks. If they'd been as practical as
artistic we might have escaped the boredom of the Dark Ages; and
the modern conveniences of the twentieth century would have been
available in the first.

   We reluctantly moved on to the later Greeks, to the great
tragedies, to the Socratic question and answer; and more by chance

than design we heard the sad story of Oedipus. I was on his side because he was given no options. If you have had the bad luck to be singled out by oracles and gods you can expect the worst. What, after all, had he done that was so very criminal? Had he deliberately killed his father? He had merely defended himself against a robber; or so he thought. And what was so disgraceful in marrying one's mother – and even that in ignorance of the fact. A mother, it seemed to me, would naturally be one's first choice. If he'd been a free agent he might have married his father as well as his mother, as I would have done without the least hesitation.

Those were my first feelings on the subject. It took me a very long time to perceive that we had been fitted out with the same pair of boots as those worn by poor old swollen-foot. The tragedy may vary with every individual but having played out the part for which we are cast we are left to grope our way, just as blindly as he did, from the stage. That, now and again, we are permitted a little triumph, a little love; that we may chance to solve a riddle, to destroy a Sphinx; that we may be lucky enough to find an Antigone or a Cordelia, or better still (unless we are hopelessly mad) an Ophelia with whom to share the burdens of our journey; to enjoy for a space the pleasures of life and divert ourselves, heedlessly, in the company of fellow clowns – serve only to highlight the horror that awaits us. Welcome though these drugs be, and greedily swallowed, they increase rather than diminish the pity and the inevitability of the drama. An occasional intermission is not enough: when the pain returns we find it worse than before; just as when the sun, shining on us for a moment from behind a mass of cloud, too brightly illuminates the awful blackness of the approaching storm.

We can only marvel how the itch for an answer was acquired, and preserved, by those pretty little bundles of fur – some of whom, resisting the lure of knowledge and not much altered by the ages, still exist to delight us in their native tree-tops or to amuse the philosopher in his hours of leisure. Had their cousins less need to specialize than other species? More food, fewer enemies? Replete and safe on some favoured tree a variety must have been produced that did not need to spend all its time on the *qui vive*. Might it not have found another use for those great big goo-goo eyes, so beautiful and so sad? Might it not have looked inwards? If, subject to the universal law, our ancestors could not have avoided such a process it would be ridiculous to praise or to blame them. But their descend-

ants, as is the way with inheritors, may grumble at the contents of
the Pandoric box they bequeathed us; and find it hard to strike a
fair balance: so much that is to our benefit along with so much that
is not. It may be true that art and science have made our lives less
boring, less uncomfortable than those of other species; but are we
happier than they? We can almost take it for granted that the
descendants of mammoths and mosquitoes will never share with us
the pleasures of aesthetic or intellectual experience. On the other
hand we can be reasonably sure that they will always be spared the
pains of consciousness, the burdens of morality, the awareness that
there is no escape from individual extinction. It is not the lark that
pours its full heart in profuse strains of unpremeditated art, but the
enraptured poet. For the bird it is no more than business as usual.
We have acquired something that distinguishes us from the beasts,
but it is a something as bitter as it is sweet. As we gaze at the beauties
of the world around us we are *aware* that they are fading even as we
look, and may wonder if our life was worth the voyage. But, according to the old legend, right at the bottom of the box, there is another
item: hope. Perhaps our ancestors, who certainly left us a lot to
hope for, are indicating that one of their descendants will discover
an antidote to death.

If any piddling philosopher is tempted to exclaim whenever I
indulge myself, quite uninstructed, in his science:

> O day and night, but this is wondrous strange!

he may ponder the riposte:

> And therefore as a stranger give it welcome.
> There are more things in heaven and earth, Horatio,
> Than are dreamt of in your philosophy.

Philosophy may be likened to an enormous forest tree with many
branches, and therefore it need not surprise us, as we amateurs make
the ascent, to find ourselves in good company with other, more
expert lovers of wisdom, right out on a limb. We, without much
trouble, and they, puffing and panting, have missed the way to the
top. The painstaking academician and the careless schoolboy are
equally well instructed in the hypotheses that at various times have
been put forward as solutions to all our troubles; and it must seem
to both groups that these are not much better than so many Aunt

Sallys, erected at a fair, for the sole purpose of being knocked down. Metaphysical, or general abstract reasoning, is not in itself fruitful; but it offers more scope for invention and embroidery than the sterile and narrow concepts of dialectical materialism or the inconsequential ravings of the existentialist. I would sooner be lost in the rich undergrowths of a jungle than in the arid wastes of a desert. The truth is, of course, that the objective can never be the same for all philosophers; and each of us is left to look for his own *summum bonum*. The sophist may be satisfied with the logical answer to a question, but what if there are many answers just as valid? The hedonist fancies pleasure as the chief good, but how to define pleasure? The stoic advises control of the passions, and so an indifference to pleasure or pain. If we could ever become indifferent to pleasure or pain should we be alive? Such indifference seems to me to be an attribute of the dead. The epicurean recommends pleasure in the pursuit of virtue, a sensuous but refined enjoyment: a worthy synthesis of the hedonistic and stoic doctrines, and one that has a certain appeal for me, if I were capable of moderation in anything.

There are so many variations on this theme that, if sufficiently interested, all we have to do is to look them up in the catalogue. But I can't resist quoting a passage I have just been reading since it curiously supports my view that one man's meat is another man's poison, and almost exactly reverses what I had to say about the universe and us.

> ... l'homme n'est qu'un roseau le plus faible de la nature, mais c'est un roseau pensant. Il ne faut pas que l'univers entier s'arme pour l'écraser; une vapeur, une goutte d'eau suffit pour le tuer; mais, quand l'univers l'écraserait l'homme serait encore plus noble que ce qui le tue, parce qu'il sait qu'il meurt, et l'avantage que l'univers a sur lui, l'univers n'en sait rien.

This notion, even from the pen of such a genius as Pascal, I find impossible to accept. I must admit it never entered my head that it could be *noble* to know that we're going to die. Are we born only to be noble, then? Am I more noble than the virus in my arsehole because I know it is killing me, and because the virus does not know what is going to kill it? I could get along better without that sort of knowledge; and I believe even the French, for all their love of honour and glory, might be prepared to sacrifice nobility for happiness. I have, of course, left myself wide open to attack by suggesting that a state of being, so rarely attained, should be the main objective of our lives. To begin with no definition of it can have a general application, at least as regards the *roseau pensant*: the universe does not think and simply is; and therefore I conclude that the happiness of other species depends simply on their being; and ours, on so many other conditions, that it is quite exceptional if we reach it at all, even for a moment. It is certainly odd that of all the organic and inorganic substances formed from the explosions of stars and the dusty pollution of space one such combination is able to think; odder still that this particular mixture of elemental gases should find it worth while to erect systems of morality, philosophy and what not – or to worry about its eventual destination. What have oxygen, nitrogen, hydrogen and carbon to do with happiness? Something very wrong somewhere. It can only be life; or rather life capable of thought, and even that too often confused by instinct. A piece of dust is better off than an animal since it is without primitive emotions, and the animals are to be envied since they are not troubled with primitive philosophies. And yet I would not be without the power to think, broken reed that I already am, since it offers so many ways of passing the time till doomsday. Perhaps we shouldn't bother about anything else, even happiness?

CHAPTER SIX

There was never a dull moment at Beaudesert as most of us were always getting into some sort of scrape. John caused us trouble as, towards the end of the term, Miss Whatley reported that his plate was missing. I think Harry must have had enough of us all by that time because, after many exclamations of rage, one of our half holidays (and one of his) was sacrificed to the search for an article that was irretrievably lost; and better lost than found. 'The whole school will look for little John's plate.' We did, including the owner who sent us cheerfully along to the rookery, round the golf course, and into the shrubbery; but strongly advised us not to search the stables as it would be a waste of time since he never went to those parts. I think myself that one day, leaning over the water-tub of famous memory, and innocently watching the larvae of mosquitoes wriggling their way to the surface, that plate, accidentally or with a little assistance, must have lost its grip on his teeth and sunk to the bottom. He kept silent on the matter so we can only guess. At any rate his timing was excellent even if he had left it a little late. Next week, plateless but personable, we were to be reunited with the parents we had not seen for a whole year.

Escorted by Miss Whatley a dozen of us Londoners, or at any rate those of us southward bound, arrived safely at Marylebone Station where our parents met us. Margaret, for once, was in a minor key and it was my father who shone brilliantly both as a chauffeur and as a guide. We stopped at Gunter's for an ice, strolled in the Park, and returned to Rumpelmeyer's for lunch; and it was here that I learnt we were to wander – a fine prospect for those who had been stationary for a year. There were exchanges on the subject of a permanent home; and although Margaret raised the usual objections my father said we might as well, without committing ourselves to anything definite, keep an eye open on our travels. If Margaret had turned against Hove he reminded her that it was at her own suggestion that they should examine the possibilities of Bedford. In the meantime, dull care should be banished and all that was required of us was to enjoy ourselves to the full. That, my father had already seen to; and it was in a spirit of languorous well-being rather than in a mood for adventure that we set forth into the wilds of Bedfordshire.

I woke with a start. Ralph had applied the brakes in a hurry, and pulled into the side. Margaret hauled John out and onto the grass verge just in time, and there he was violently sick. There was absolutely no clowning about it except, perhaps, for the rusticity of the surroundings: none of that ambiguous mixture of the comic and tragic. From the time he had been relieved of his plate he had instantly ceased to wear the motley; and his performance now, considering the angle at which Margaret was daintily holding him by the seat of his trousers over a ditch, was as dignified as it was natural. Our troop had gained an actor capable of playing a tragic part, but we had not lost the necessary clown. It was not I that filled that subtle role – I was just a fool, fit for folly, and my mishaps pre-dictably my own fault – but my father. He never had the least intention of what he would have called making 'an arse' of himself, though he was always ready to entertain his company mildly if also instructively. He could be quite comic in a decent way, and it was so decent that his jokes and puns amused drawing-rooms more than clubs. His kindly approach and his good natured sympathy made him, however, popular everywhere. Just the sort, in fact, a simple, gentle creature, on whom the gods, when they noticed him, were likely to play a few scurvy tricks; and they had made a good start when they introduced him to Margaret.

What could provide a better example of the minor part my father was to play than the events of this outing? He had set forth to give us all a wonderful treat. Perhaps he had been unwise to pile Rumpelmeyer on Gunter, but how was he to know that those delicious ices and meringues were destined for a ditch? John had as eagerly accepted them in the first instance as he now, on second thoughts, rejected them. I had gone to sleep, and Margaret had taken almost as little interest in the beauties of Bedfordshire as I had. Why, she now enquired, had he insisted on curry when a wholesome plaice or a breast of chicken might have held it all down? Personally I doubt if even a bucket of lead would have done that. But the trials of our unlucky cicerone were by no means over.

When we set out again my mother retired to the back with John and I received a double promotion. To be in front was almost as if one were the driver; and watching my father's movements carefully I pretended that, in case of trouble, I could pull on the handbrake and with the other hand on the wheel perhaps keep us on the road till we had come to a halt. My father noticed my interest and began on the workings of a combustion engine which he seemed to know about quite as thoroughly as Mr Nathan. Obviously one couldn't even start without an engine in good condition, but it was only the driving that excited me. He saw, after a bit, that the lecture was going in at one ear and out of the other; and, always hoping to please, suggested that I might like to try my skill with the map. I could look at the signposts and relate them to our position while he just drove on. He indicated vaguely that we were somewhere in south-east England, north of London, and probably west of it. There were several towns of a sort thereabouts and any of them would give us a line on Bedford.

At the next signpost we discovered that a place called St Neots was five miles off and Cambridge twenty. But my father was much more interested in a notice tied to the post with a bit of string.

July 30th 1912, For one day only,
At the Rectory Field near St Neots:
BROWN'S CIRCUS
The Greatest Show On Earth.

'Now that's what I call a bit of luck. Yesterday or tomorrow, and we should have missed it. We need to relax after all our trials. Just get a good laugh. Needn't stay long.'

'I simply don't know what you're talking about.'

'A circus, my dear. I don't think the boys have ever seen one.'

'Well, John's not going to see this one. Nor am I.'

'But Daddy and I can, can't we, Mum? Oh do say, yes!'

'After all, Margaret, it *is* the first day of the hols.'

'I should have thought there'd been enough excitement for most of us already; and Dick looks a little pale. Go, if you must, but please don't overdo it.'

'Good old Mumbo-Jumbo.'

My father was as pleased with this permission as I was, and light-heartedly burst into song as we drove on.

> 'So one fine day he ran away
> To join a travelling circus;
> Sleeping sometimes on the ground,
> And sometimes in the wirkus.'

Up to now Ralph had always been rather a shadowy figure in my life, hardly ever on the scenes. As a person full of gaiety and life, active and boyish, slightly mad and yet very much on the spot, I had never seen him before. This was the sort of father I wanted, and I knew I could not have found a better one. It was a pity that he, too, was always running away to join a travelling circus; but while I had him I was going to make the most of him. I was trembling with anticipation as, hand in hand, we hurried into the Big Top.

Lasciate ogni speranza, voi ch'entrate. I had not yet evolved my system for dealing with treats. At that age I was far too optimistic, and often sadly disillusioned. I am not complaining about the quality of the performance or the merit of the performers. My father could, indeed, compare Mr Brown's establishment with Mr Barnum's, and his clowns with such as Grimaldi and Dan Leno; and he would not have imagined that he was going to see the greatest show on earth. All I knew for certain was that this was a circus, something I had never seen before, and quite different from a fair.

I was put off at once by the stench. An overpowering *pot-pourri* of human and animal stinks was topped up by the indescribable smell of fear: acrid, rank, mephitic; and was discharged only by the animals. They were frightened and humiliated; and the tricks they performed to loud guffaws, the clothes they wore, deprived them of the beauty they had a right to exhibit and made them look, if that were possible, uglier than the clowns. I was not too young to be aware of their suffering. I instantly took sides with them, suffered with them, and was as frightened as they were. At the crack of a whip a cringing dog adorned with something round its neck resembling an Elizabethan ruff, jumped desperately, blindly, through a hoop covered with paper. It came trotting round, wagging its tail. It had once again escaped the whip. How clever it was! But there had been many a time, before it had learnt what was expected of it, when the wretched creature had not got off so lightly. The elephant, on the near approach of any human being, with or without the whip, rose ponderously on its hind legs and shuffled about in what was supposed to be a dance: an ignoble spectacle. And the ponies, on whose backs ladies in spangled tights stood or leapt carelessly from one to another of them, moved woodenly, unnaturally round the ring so that their riders might the less likely fall off. A perverted chimpanzee, popular with the crowd, got many cheap laughs for the indignities it administered to its equals and for the humiliations it had to put up with at the commands of its betters. An uneasy part it had to play, but not its fault. And perhaps, dressed as a clown, and holding so invidious a rank in the evolutionary scale, half-way between the lower and higher orders, it could hope to be nothing more than an obscene travesty of both. Now Chimpy would brandish a hoop in front of a stray dog which, encouraged by menacing gestures, obediently leapt through it; and the next moment, at the crack of a whip, he himself would jump on to a stand, wave a Union Jack, and make a clumsy salute. With an impertinent slap on the elephant's trunk he would cause it to dance for his pleasure only to be ordered to join a string of cartwheeling clowns and dance for ours. So many smells had already made me feel queer and now, trying to take in all these activities, I began to feel distinctly dizzy.

Mr Brown gave us far too much for our money and reminded me, as he stood belligerently in the middle of the ring, of Auntie Lou. On the top storey, so to speak, artistes swooped from trapeze to trapeze, sometimes only saved from certain death by clutching at the hands of others. On a lower level, just out of reach of the elephant's trunk, a tight-rope walker with the aid of a balancing pole, ran lightly to and fro, stumbling on occasion to give us a thrill; and he was often aped by the ape who did it all much more naturally. The ground floor accommodated the rest of the troupe, and the ground itself the clowns; either because they were genuinely tired or, more likely, were overacting their parts. They could hardly stand upright for a moment and, even when the going looked good, fell heavily over an imaginary pin. One of these hideous creatures advanced towards me and seized me by the hand. His intentions may have been friendly, as he suggested I might like to ride on his shoulders round the ring. Ralph bailed me out at the cost of another shilling. But this narrow escape acted as a catalytic agent. All pressures were suddenly removed; and stumbling in the footsteps of the clown I reached the ring-side and made the best possible use of that arena as a vomitorium. As regards sounds and smells I contributed all I had of both for the benefit of the public; but my performance, like most of my other stage appearances, went unnoticed. From the miseries of that inferno my father dragged me out into the heavenly freshness of a summer afternoon.

'You've been wonderfully quick, you two. Did you enjoy yourselves?'

'Not as much as we might have done. Rather a poor show, so we came out when we'd had enough of it.'

'Ralph! You don't mean to say – '

'I was sicker than John, Mummy.'

'Rot! You couldn't have been.'

'I did warn you, Ralph. All that excitement coming on top of – '

'I know, my dear, I'm sorry. He was all right to start with.'

'But he's lost his plate, too! I wonder I didn't notice it before. At least you could nip back and retrieve it.'

'I really don't think I could, Margaret. No, I could not. There doesn't seem much wrong with their teeth, anyhow, thanks to your foresight.'

My mother was mollified. John and I changed places, and my father drove on. He got us safely to St Neots which he declared to be very central and on the main road to Bedford. He must have got bored with the main road, or taken a short cut. We arrived that evening and spent the next few days at a little place called Woburn Sands.

I had noticed, of course, that Margaret was subdued. There was a reason for her depression, that could be laid, fairly and squarely, on the fiend Pippa. If my mother did not exactly know what sister and weak, deceitful brother were plotting she must have suspected it. Next day Ralph drove her dutifully into Bedford where they spent the whole day with estate agents and even inspected what houses were on offer. He readily took her around visiting those of her friends who lived in the district; and even pretended – the monster – that neither houses nor friends were quite so dilapidated as she made them out to be. By being so liberal he was taking not the slightest risk of Margaret settling in Bedford. He knew she hated the country, and there would have been nothing to occupy her in a little county town. But, much more to the point, there was a letter in his pocket from Pippa who, on a hasty visit to Hove, had been prompt and efficient. One estate agent was enough for her, and also one house. She may not even have had the time to look at it. At least it was a house; and she had taken it on a seven years lease. No wonder my father was in such good spirits. Cats and kittens once securely mewed up a mouse might play; though it would still have to go to India to be on the safe side.

When our parents returned from their house-hunting we bitterly complained that there was absolutely nothing to do in Woburn Sands, and that we had done it all in one day. We should have been in for a dreary weekend if my father had not come up with two good ideas. We should all go into the woods with note-books and write down everything we saw. Prizes for those who saw the most, or the rarest; and then, on Sunday, we could make an expedition to Bedford not to visit the estate agents unless we met them by chance on the river: a-rowing we would go on the Lim-popo, known in England as the Great Ouse.

Margaret's notebook was a complete blank, she had looked for nothing but snakes and had seen none; and apparently nothing else either. Ralph did not enter the competition. At the end of a ride we startled a fox which I recorded as such and John as a 'woof'. My father explained that the last wolf had come to a bad end more than two hundred years ago: John obstinately maintained that his had not as anybody could see for themselves. It was three hundred years old, and as it could run quite well might live for another three hundred. We sank to rest beneath a tree while the argument expanded to an unconscionable length. We heard that it did not have a tail, that it did; that it had a brush because it was a fox; that it had a tail because it was a woof. If my father lost this argument – and it seemed likely – John would score heavily with such a rare creature in his book. My only hope was in numbers. As I lay on the ground a string of ants began to climb up inside my trousers. I counted seventeen of them before their tickling became too much to bear. If John could get away with a wolf, I might be just as lucky with an emmet.

It was now that Ralph, still perhaps a little inspired by the feats of acrobats, or possibly in an effort to break off a fruitless argument, or simply from a superabundance of high spirits, took off his coat and began to climb the tree around which the rest of us lay exhausted. It was not a difficult tree, a larch or fir, and was provided with many convenient and richly carpeted branches. Every time he paused we encouraged him with shouts of 'Higher, Daddy, higher.' He reached the top; and all might have been well if he had not recklessly let go with one hand and waved to us vaingloriously with the other. Even as we cheered he began the involuntary descent, preceded by his glasses. As I dashed to retrieve them Margaret issued orders. I was to come out from under at once, and Ralph was to stop it. I did as I was told but Ralph didn't, couldn't, though it was clear he was trying to. Blind as a bat he clutched at every branch he passed, failed to hang on to it and was gently deposited on the one below. His approach to us was slow and even dignified, but inevitable. He was subject to the law of gravity from which, I'm sorry to say, we were totally released. Just as the unlucky victim of a banana skin is greeted with heartless peals of laughter so we welcomed Ralph when he at last could go no further. He was smiling bravely when he reached *terra firma*. Neither he nor his glasses were damaged.

At the end of the day my father, without much thought, agreed that seventeen emmets were, give or take a few, of equal importance to a woof; and each of us received a shilling for our labours.

Ralph was not deterred by his arboreal misadventure from pursuing a reckless career on the river. He drove us into Bedford, and under the bridge he hired a skiff, or whatever it might be called, and we embarked on a voyage of discovery down stream. We started leisurely enough with my father getting the feel of the oars and my mother the feel of the rudder, while John and I got the feel of the water. All we did was to splash our hands in it but this so disturbed Margaret, who thought we were about to fall in, that in clutching at us she abandoned her duties at the helm and we ploughed our way into a thick bed of bulrushes. Very thrilling, but it took Ralph a long time to extricate us. I offered to steer once we got out into the river again so that Mumbo-Jumbo could have a nice rest and attend to her parasol; and I fancy she and Ralph would have accepted the offer if John hadn't instantly suggested that he could do it better than I could. This confused the issue until it was resolved, after many heated exchanges, in the usual inefficient way by each of us being allotted a guide-rope. What could anyone hope to do with the command of half a tiller? To keep a ship on its course is a delicate job which requires sensitivity, timing, and swift decision. It does not require strength. With another boat advancing on us and with my father labouring away, ignorant of danger, we were quite helpless since it was as much as I could do to prevent John taking us to port and as much as he could do to stop me taking us to starboard. By exerting all our strength we held on a straight, if a collision, course which was avoided at the last moment by the dextrous manoeuverings of a boatman in charge of a cargo of care-free trippers. 'We should have hired a man, too,' my mother remarked. My father rested on his oars, mopped his brow and said nothing.

Although Ralph had paused to recover his breath the stream softly carried us along, and softly I wish it had till, on that gentle note, I could end my song. But our speed increased, at first most mysteriously, and we found ourselves sailing faster without my father's assistance than with it. As the banks rushed past us we became aware of a sinister roaring sound ahead which became louder and louder as we approached it.

'Can you hear something strange, Ralph?'

'I can.'

'Do you think we are going in the right direction?'

'It doesn't sound like it. Perhaps we'd better pull over to the other side.'

'For goodness sake, Ralph, don't just talk. Do something. It might be a waterfall.'

'Now, keep calm, Margaret. It's only a weir.'

'Did you see what was written on that post, Daddy?'

'Which one, Dick?'

'The one we've just passed.'

'No, what did it say?'

'DANGER.'

There was a wicked sparkle in John's eyes.

'If we go down a weir, I expect we'll all get drowned.'

'There now, Ralph, you see you've upset them both.'

Muttering to himself my father dug his oars into the water and with might and main edged his way out of the current until at last we found ourselves in what appeared to be a tideless backwater. We had escaped from the sound and fury of the untamed river and entered one of the narrow prisons where it was caged. We were poised on the river's roof, the sun shone brightly upon us, and we had the happy feeling of those who had greatly adventured and had survived to tell the tale. This state of elation did not last long. Behind us the lock-keeper was turning a wheel, as we noticed that our exit that way was being barred by heavy underwater gates. In front of us the man more slowly turned another wheel, and those gates, with horrid groans and gurglings, began to release not us but the watery support that had kept us in the world of the living. Slowly we sank down into the depths where rank weeds grew on the dripping walls, and dankness and darkness prevailed. In spite of Margaret drawing our attention, while she could still see them, to the pretty flowers of the lock-keeper's garden, and eventually to his boots so far above us; in spite of my father's explaining the principles of locks and that they served the same purpose as lifts, getting you comfortably and safely from one floor to another without the need to use stairs or weirs as the case might be, John began to howl that he wanted to get out, and I too felt very melancholy. Although I did not give way to tears I agreed silently with his opinion that whatever the risks in shooting the rapids we should at least have been able to see where we were going, comforted by warmth and light. As we sank steadily down Margaret must have been a little influenced by John's views as she advised us not to breathe. Did Ralph think the air quite wholesome? I have forgotten his reply, but he was likely to have pronounced it better than nothing. Whatever the state of the atmosphere in that lock, as soon as we were released on to the river's next floor, we all cheered up and took great gulps of undoubtedly the purest air in the world.

The human spirit can rise as fast as it can sink. We had hardly got going again when I wanted to row. I hastily added, before John could get in *his* oar, that he would have great fun in doing all the steering by himself. My father had the sense not to surrender more than one of them to me. We sat side by side and at first I found that I had exactly the same trouble with him as I had had with John. He would persist in laying a hand on mine, so that I had to engage in a struggle not only with the Ouse but with Ralph. He said it would be better, before I tried by myself, if I got the hang of it: it was really a question of rhythm. So for a few minutes we rowed quietly on. But it was not a question of rhythm, of in out, in out, that appealed to me. That was far too slow and steady for me. I was all for speed. As soon as he relinquished his share of my oar I proved I was a good deal faster than he was by rowing three and sometimes three-and-a-half strokes to his one. If Margaret hadn't suddenly suggested that I looked tired I might not have come to grief. To show her that I was far from being exhausted and attempting to get in a fourth stroke I missed the water entirely and fell over backwards, losing the oar at the same time. My father had a really good laugh at somebody else's expense for a change, and told me I had caught a crab. When we at length retrieved the oar, I searched the blade carefully but there was no sign of my catch. It had had plenty of time to escape.

While all this action was going on our helmsman, much more interested in the spectacle before his eyes than in the direction we were taking, had grossly neglected his duties. Even so we were a little surprised to find ourselves within a few yards of the lock which, by rights, we should have left miles behind. We had come full circle and perhaps more than once. It was certainly not a new one because we all recognized the lock-keeper who asked us, with a grin on his face, which way we intended to go now? Margaret said we'd had enough and should make tracks for home before the mist of the evening, beautiful mist, had a chance to suffocate us; and Ralph instantly agreed. Luckily for us the keeper, enthralled by our performance, had turned a blind eye on a flotilla waiting to go down stream and a deaf ear to the cries of rage that issued from it, so that his empty tank received us at once. But now it held no terror for me though its appearance was just as forbidding. There is a very great difference between descending into a tomb and resurrection from it, a gloomy finality in the one case and a bright beginning in the other. As those walls shrunk away, as we left the forlorn depths of Avernus and approached the gates of Heaven, I felt happier and happier; and the contrast between these two scenes made an impression on me that has lasted to this day: but I would not call it traumatic. Locks and lifts I can use in both directions although I feel much more comfortable going up in them than down.

On recollecting the events of this little tour I am convinced that the various mishaps which I suffered only added to its pleasures. If all had gone calmly, I should not have enjoyed it half so much. Now, of course, exactly the opposite holds good. Even a broken shoe-lace when out on a walk is a disaster of the first order. I have never had the foresight to carry a spare and, supposing I had, to bend and balance on one leg, to insert the new one, is no longer so simple as it sounds. No, the more ordinary the excursion the better I like it. Nothing has ever induced me to revisit a circus; and the very thought of catching a crab fills me with alarm.

The next day, meandering as was his wont, Ralph conducted us without incident to our terminus in Hove.

CHAPTER SEVEN

Am I boldly to state that my father, throughout this prolonged period of intrigue and deception, never suffered from the pangs of conscience? It looks as if I must. Outwardly, his features bore the stamp of innocence and health. He appeared to have absolutely nothing on his mind except how best to please us all. Cheerfulness and good humour never failed him from morning to night. But guilt that transmogrifies into gaiety is a gift denied to most of us; and very welcome to those within the ambit of the afflicted. In this respect my father resembled his brothers and sisters. They were decent enough not to expect the world to share the burden of their sins, and they were always at their most charming and sympathetic when they behaved to that world in a way that something, somewhere, insisted was not altogether altruistic.

I much prefer to be conned by charmers than by sulky incompetents whose shifty eyes and bludgeoning tactics, accompanied by whining complaints as to their hard lot, make it quite clear that they can't be bothered to respect one's dignity or to recognize that one is a human being with feelings much more likely to be wounded than their own. I am reminded of that taxi-driver (and can compare his courteous approach with that of the Stracheys) who met us with eager welcome at the Termini after an atrocious day spent crawling along the coast from Cannes to Rome. Cold and exhausted we had fought off a milling crowd of angry, shouting cabbies trying to get our custom, and had reached the wet and deserted Piazza dei Cinquecento when he gently relieved us of our cases saying they were much too heavy for us to carry, welcomed us warmly to the big city and darted towards an enormous limousine, not parked with the other taxis and, as I saw at once, without a meter on it. I gave him the address of our hotel, in the Bocca di Leone, and asked him to drive slowly as I was troubled by my back. He held my hand in sympathy; he knew what it was to be in pain. He would take us, moreover, on a special route that would avoid sharp corners and unnecessary changes of gear. Instead of a direct approach down the Tritone we made a sort of circular tour round Rome at midnight; and in a steady drizzle he had the kindness (and cheek) to point out the Colosseum as we passed it (more imposing at that hour, all the same, than at any other). We were now further from the Hotel d'Inghilterra than we had been at the station. Wondering if he proposed to take us to the Catacombs I groaned aloud. This he heard, stopped at once, and hurried to arrange a cushion (the very same one that had been supporting his own back) for my greater comfort. Eventually we arrived at the place of execution, as one always does sooner or later; and to soften the blow or – ungentlemanly brute that I am to suggest it – to exclude the hotel porter from our conversation he lowered his voice and gently, but not apologetically announced his charges.

'*Due mille*,' I exclaimed in a passion. 'Ridiculous!'

With a glance at the porter he put one finger to his lips and murmured: 'Consider what a beautiful evening we have spent together! We have seen Rome at her best. How far and how softly we have driven and how careful we have been of that poor back! The lady is now quite relaxed after the tiring journey. How can one put a price on such items as I have been privileged to offer?' He shrugged his shoulders. 'The English gentleman will give me what he thinks fit.' The English mug paid up in full; and after a round of embraces we entered the hotel conscious of a warm glow of pleasure and gratitude for the welcome Rome had bestowed upon us. And this was not diminished by the porter's sullen remark that we had paid five times the legal fare. Many, envious of the Stracheys, have attempted to convince me of their deceptive devices for mugging the stranger in their midst – but in vain. Drives round Rome, or through life with my uncles and aunts, were priceless for me. To be taken for a ride is not always a disaster.

My father took us for many that summer. Margaret was in a restless mood, bored by Hove and the Mulhollands, and probably disturbed at the thought that as a matron with three children she could hardly hope to compete much longer with a younger generation of beauties for the favours of the military in India. That last trip of hers had not gone with the usual swing. But if she now was expected to settle down there might be places, even in West Sussex, that would offer more worldly delights than dreary old Hove. So, with this as an excuse, we spent a whole week in Bognor; and found it wanting.

We stayed a little longer at Worthing which, at first, seemed more promising. But here my inventive mind got us into trouble. I may have seen a land-boat with sails scudding along the sands; and I soon fixed up a portion of sheet on my scooter. Before a full sou'wester I and my machine flew along the promenade causing the maximum of discomfort to the retired. With only one hand to steer with and the other holding on tight to a flapping sail, and the sail itself totally obscuring my view, I was a real menace to myself and others; and complaints were lodged. We disregarded these, or rather my mother did, until one day I flew over the edge of the esplanade and landed on a pebble beach; and after this accident Margaret declared that Worthing was far too dangerous a place for children – and no doubt, while we were there, for the elderly too. So for the rest of those hols we settled at Hove.

The scheme Ralph and Pippa were hatching that summer, even though it utterly miscarried, was comparatively simple and superficial. Pippa, when she told me about it years later, went off into shrieks of laughter; and I don't suppose my father took it any more seriously. It seems there had been a misunderstanding entirely due to the stupidity of the agent. That incompetent man of business wanted a signature in exchange for the lease. Pippa, merely an agent herself, could not be expected to sign it. She had done what was expected of her, had taken the house for seven years and had, moreover, told my father she had done so. She omitted to tell him that he would have to go along and sign the lease himself. When, at length, he paid that visit, he discovered that the agent had feebly allowed another client, on the the grounds that he was prepared to sign a totally unnecessary document, to take over the lease. We lost a house that none of us was ever destined to see, let alone to live in; and a very good opportunity to put a term to Margaret's wanderings permanently. Confronted with a *fait accompli* the victim hardly ever escapes its consequences. But for the best results the *fait* really should be *accompli*.

One day Mr Mulholland, with evident distaste and disapproval, handed my father several postcards sent out by the enterprising manufacturers of Black and White whisky. On them were a number of black shapes imposed on a white background, and we were told to cut them out, join them together, and they would resolve themselves into an elephant which would win a prize of fifty pounds. Easy, I thought; and set to work. There before me, in next to no time, lay a trunk, a tiny tail, a pair of huge ears, an authentic leg and foot and a sausage of a body on which these articles could be hung and glued. But surely an elephant is a quadruped? Then why did ours have only one leg and one foot? Something wrong somewhere, or else Messrs Black and White were pulling three of our legs and three of our feet. Ralph thought this unlikely as their customers, in a fury, would certainly turn to a smoother and less irritating brand. We spent the evening shuffling my elephant about, and though at times it looked more or less like one, it always remained terribly deformed. John's elephant had the merit of being comic. He had transposed its trunk and tail. My father studied both of these efforts, but was not to be hurried into committing himself. He said he would sleep on it.

The next morning Ralph proved himself to be the genius we all knew he was. He carefully, despite our warnings, cut out only the *white* bits; and sure enough, before we went to bed, there was an elephant complete in every detail, and ready to be dispatched to the makers. We wondered if a white elephant counted. Was there such an animal? He assured us he was perfectly familiar with them; and, if I wasn't then quite convinced that he was, I am now. Could there be one other brain in all England capable of solving such a puzzle? When, a week later, he received a postal order for five shillings, we discovered that there were no less than two hundred in the same class as his.

I have often wished I could arrive at a fixed portrait of my parents, to say to myself, 'Yes, that's what they were like,' to pin them down on the setting board of memory and study their characteristics at leisure. The members of a species – a term invented for the convenience of naturalists – are supposed to differ only in minor details; and in the beginning it was obviously intended that they should not differ at all. We have it on the highest authority that the earth brought forth the beast of the earth after his kind. But in art as in life the creature has plenty of time in which, perversely, to thwart the work of the creator; and every single specimen, especially in the case of homo sapiens, now dares so wildly to vary from the original norm that none can be assumed to be typical. Even a Black elephant, for example, can transpose itself into a White one without the least consideration for the scientist; and human beings, of course, are far more difficult to piece together than a jig-saw jumbo. Occasionally, I have discovered in the puzzle of my parents, a shape – be it a mood, a thought, a posture or an action – that seems to be worth cutting out for assembly into the finished portrait. But then, other oddities of behaviour have revealed themselves as no less characteristic, and room must be found for them too; so that, at times, I have felt the work would never be done. I can only hope that by recording all I remember of them something of what they were like will be recovered.

My mother, although emotionally unstable, was more predictable than my father. Her reactions to the simplest situations were always grotesque, and it could at least be taken for granted they would be. While I can agree with her view that my father was a weak man but very, very sweet, a view sustained by her genuine love for him, it was only half the story. If she had not been blinded by that love she must have discovered that there was another side to his character which, so far as she was concerned, was often disloyal and even treacherous. He never behaved so cynically towards others, simply because those others, less intimately connected with him, could be appeased with words of sympathy and hastily forgotten if they expected anything more. If my father was, at times, quite ruthless in his dealings with Margaret I think she herself acted as the catalysing agent for such a change in his normal pattern of behaviour. The forces of disorder were not to be endured by Ralph. Rather than face the inevitable emotional storm that any open discussion on even the most trivial matter was bound to raise he soon discovered that relations with Margaret were calmer if he acted behind her back. She was far more 'scrupious' in this respect than he was; but his reasons for deceiving her were, it seems to me, more or less valid though I was myself, frequently, an additional victim. It is hard to feel anything but sympathy for those who, by whatever means, attempt to loosen the ties of family life. And yet it was my father who shocked me. The uncertain temper of a tigress is to be expected and so one gets used to it. But to come across a hare, a charming animal generally only glimpsed as it scuds across a field, positively standing up and *boxing* is a most unnerving spectacle.

Dr Dill, after more than seventy years of practice, was slowly beginning to discharge his patients with clean bills of health, and advice to go to younger men. He had managed to disembarrass himself of a huge clientele, but his relations with us had always been of such a curious and intimate complexity that he could not bring himself to write us off his books. I believe that I myself was the very last patient he ever attended professionally, and I'm glad to report that he ended his career with a most successful, if unorthodox, treatment. I must explain how it arose.

But, in considering that last sentence, I see that's just what I can't explain. I can only put on record the disease and its cure. Towards the end of those hols I woke one morning horrified to discover that during the night I had developed a bone between my legs where previously there had been no more than a comfortable and easily manipulated (perhaps, not quite the right word to use considering my age) piece of indiarubber. What I mean to say is that things must have got to a sorry pass when it just was not possible to get one's cock into a pair of trousers. We did our best. Almost everyone wrestled with the trousers, but in vain. During the course of the morning it became quite clear that only Dr Dill could get them on; and if he failed then Ralph would have to go out and buy a larger pair – a solution which might not have resolved the problem as, even naked, I found it curiously uncomfortable to walk. Was I to spend the rest of my life bent double? At last, in despair, we sent for our doctor. When Tom, his chauffeur, reinforced by the shocked Mr Mulholland, got him upstairs, (after a short pause for recovery of breath) the first thing he did was to laugh loudly. This was in itself reassuring as he usually did so when called in by us. He then ordered a bucket of cold water to be prepared.

'Tepid, Doctor?' suggested old Nanny.

'Certainly not. Let the tap run for a few minutes. I don't care in the least how cold it is. The colder the better.'

He was never a man to take half measures. He would go to any lengths where his patients were concerned. His only regret now was that he could not in person apply the prescribed treatment. To lift that bucket was beyond his strength.

'No matter. You, Tom, put the boy in the bath and pour it over the afflicted part; and if it doesn't work the first time fill another and repeat as often as you like, until it does.'

One bucket, accurately directed by Tom, was enough for the 'afflicted part' and more than enough for me. As the young man, who seemed to be over zealous, was preparing another dose, I escaped with a yelp from the operating theatre; and while I was successfully getting into my trousers, all could see that we had been spared a journey to Lourdes. On occasion Dr Dill could bring off a miracle with the best of them.

We escorted him to his car; and Mr Mulholland, who had been dismissed and was still in the dark as to the nature of the disease earnestly enquired if it were infectious.

'Vexatious? For the boy, possibly. For you and me, Mr Mulholland, I can guarantee immunity and also, now I come to think of it (he allowed himself a senile chuckle), for Mrs Mulholland. Home, Tom.'

I have suffered a good deal from this particular manifestation of Nature. It could be called precocious then, and at all times, vexatious. We can agree it's contagious, but is it also infectious? However profound my studies became on this interesting illness I was always convinced that fundamentally the doctor's cure was the most efficacious. But I soon discovered there were other, and much more pleasurable, ways of damping down Nature than by douches of cold water. This was not the last we saw of Dr Dill, but professionally we allowed him to rest on his laurels; and on the whole I think he had earned them.

CHAPTER EIGHT

I have already noted that, during those summer holidays, Margaret was far less flamboyant than usual; and quite mistakenly I put it down, if not exactly to old age, then to a certain consciousness of the sobriety expected of a matron. There may have been something of this in her mind but, if so, I now have proof that it produced more than enough adrenalin to guarantee that her dancing days were by no means over. A conspirator works silently and shuns advertisement as does a cat when stalking its prey. The first, and the last, the victims know of it is the sudden pounce. How could mice like Ralph and Pippa ever have thought to bell such a creature? While they were plotting her downfall she was calmly plotting Ursula's. The prospect of pleasure in the minds of young officers is likely to be damped if the appurtenances of marriage, such as babies, nappies and ayahs, are too obviously displayed – though, luckily, a husband generally has a stimulating effect on them. Ursula, therefore, had to be dumped, and at the end of those holidays dumped she was. I don't know where. I can only guess as I lost sight of her for a considerable time. To be quite fair to Margaret it must be remembered that, for Ursula, a return to India might have been fatal; and if there is the further objection that, even so, it was her duty to look after the child in England a plea could be entered that almost anyone would have done it better. And is not, her counsel might have added, a wife's first duty to her husband? Extenuating circumstances can almost always be found if one looks for them. I'm glad she was allowed a last fling. So there was a general dispersal of the family. As soon as John and I returned home to school, Ralph set sail for India – accompanied by Margaret: the biters most comprehensively bit.

I have recently been left, as a result of a very unexpected but strangely moving event, a number of early photographs and a packet of my schoolboy letters written at this time to my parents. In reading them over I was gratified to see that some facts I had previously noted from memory were confirmed by contemporary evidence – though I can't imagine what induced my mother to keep these mementoes of the past. She intensely disliked personal objects and by the time she was relieved of the last burden of all, herself, she had, so I thought, been relieved of everything else. But these she had, most unfortunately for herself and Margery Richardson, over-looked. They revealed a complicity of interest and a betrayal of privacy which, since I'm trying to get at the facts of my life, I shall have to reveal in my turn.

On the backs of some of these letters of mine what more natural for one in a hurry, or provident of paper, than to write a note to my mother? Margery Richardson may have felt confident that such a liberty would receive no adverse comment from her correspondent in India. But I condemn it strongly even though, in my case, indignation is of little avail sixty years after the crime. Can one really believe that Margery's eyes resisted the easily read contents of the original letters?

In the first of these letters (Nov. 19. 1912) I informed Dear Mummy (a) about the ceremonies connected with the Guy and (b) added a few elementary observations on Natural History to give substance to the correspondence. 'It has not snowed yet. The leaves are coming off very quickly now, but later on they will be all off.' Nothing for Mrs Richardson to worry about in that. And I feel sure that my mother would hardly have preserved this letter if it had not been endorsed by another of greater interest: Margery wrote on the back of it: 'I have been asked to have Mrs Russell and Julia for a little visit in the holidays and said I would if Julia had not been *near* any illness.' The Richardsons were in advance of their times, but I don't think it ever seriously entered their heads to set up a co-educational establishment; although I remember that Enid and a perfectly horrid little friend of hers called Rosemary began to attend classes to our dismay. I suppose word had got round to the effect that unwanted Strachey children of either sex might find asylum at Beaudesert Park – a suggestion that Julia's father would eagerly have followed up. My mother must have been at the bottom of this intrigue; but the odd couple never found a permanent resting place with us. From time to time they put in an appearance and then vanished. I imagine that Julia too often went near illness for comfort's sake, and that the Richardsons found Auntie Lou quite uneducable.

In another letter I describe our Christmas Day festivities, food and presents in abundance. Towards the end of it I write: 'I had a lovely book of Photographs of Ursula in Kensington Gardens they were so nice. I had a box of Meccano from Aunt Pippa. And John and I are having a lovely time and so is everybody else here. With much love from Dickey.' On the back of *that* letter my mother seems to have suffered a reverse. Margery writes: 'Dearest Mrs Strachey' (a peculiar opening) 'All's well. The weather has turned *very* cold and snow is on the ground. We think it would be very risky for the Baby to come here under the circumstances and might just upset her – so sorry as I am to disappoint you I think it best not to attempt it. The boys are as lively as possible. Much love from Mrs Richardson' (a peculiar ending).

In all these letters there is no suggestion that I felt in any way deprived by my parents' absence, and they show on the contrary, what my memory has already brought back to me, that I thoroughly enjoyed my schooldays at Beaudesert Park; and also my school holidays at the same address. I shall include here a couple as typical of any normal boy's correspondence.

> Beaudesert Park
> Henley-in-Arden
> Jan. 18. 1913
>
> My dear Daddy and Mummy
>   I hope you have had a very happy new year. I am sending you a story, though it is not very good, I hope you will like it. I will send you a maze next week, it will be my very difficult one, which I am sure will puzzle you. A few days ago we went to see a hunt, John saw the Fox, and a minute or two afterwards we saw the hounds in full cry. The term will begin on thursday. Mr Richardson has bought a new shot gun besides his rifle. Mrs Richardson and Austin have gone down to Brighton and will come back with the boys. Robert had two shots with Mr Richardson's shot gun, but he missed them both, they were wood pigeons. I hope you are both quite well. With much love from Dickey.

If only the maze had survived I should have copied it out since, apart from photographs, my work would otherwise have remained

Cousin Julia

Dick, in Bognor

Beaudesert Park, Henley-in-Arden

Beaudesert Park: the cricket ground

unillustrated. But as I eventually became a writer, even if, judged by professional standards I did not make a living out of it (or anything else, come to that), I shall include that story.

Another adventur of Sherlock Homes
Chapter 1

"I do wish Watson would hurry up" said Sherlock Homes to himself, "he has taken about three-quarters of an hour already his breakfast will be all cold"

About a quarter of an hour later Watson came down and instantly said, "I say old chap look here this looks rather interesting. He pointed to a Paragraph in the "Daily Mail".

This is what Sherlock Homes saw;

Mysterious Murder of a certain Mrs Hutchinson. Mr Hutchinson himself narrowly escaped being killed too.

Mr Hutchinson says that the Man who murdered Mrs Hutchinson had a mask on his face so he did not see who it was.

"Well" said Sherlock Homes "I think we might as well go and see who it is really dont you"

"Rather" ejaculated Watson "I am simply longing for something exciting to do"

"Look here" said Homes "get your revolvers and cartrigdes, I will get mine then we shall be all right. I think it is best to take up our lodgings in the same flat and the same room as Mr and Mrs Hutchinson did. I will be Mr Hutchinson. You will be my servant. Mr G. Hands.

"Right you are" laughed Watson "I hope we shall have some fun."

Chapter 2

At seven o'clock in the evening Mr Holmes and Dr Watson were seen to enter the room's of Mr Hutchinson.

"Look here" said Holmes stand up on that chair and hide yourself as well as you can while I get into Mrs Hutchinsons bed. dont let anyone see you for goodness sake."

"All right" said Watson and he got on to the chair and hid himself as well a he could.

At twelv o'clock there was a tap-tap. tap– and then a sliding noise annonced that a trap door was being brought into action. Then suddenly a head and shoulders appeared and then out came the body and legs and the man advanced towards Holmes's bed.

But suddenly Watson said "Hands up and the man turned round and Watson saw two gleaming eyes in the darkness instantly Watson turned on the electric light and rushed at the man and hit him as hard as he could under the chin at the same time Sherlock jumped out of Bed. But very soon afterwards another man and yet another man jumped out and Rushed towards Sherlock Homes and Dr Watson after having faught for five minutes without any advantage on either side up the stair's came

some policemen and soon the other two men were bound and gagged. Sherlock Holmes, Dr Watson, and 2 or three other policemen marched the prisoner up to the Police station. The sentence was they had to be put into prison for Manslaughter for 15 years.
I am sure that Sherlock Holmes and Dr Watson will have some more Adventures

Margaret and Ralph, whatever the former may have said from time to time in her letters, remained for what seemed ages in India. The next letter comes from the winter term.

> Beaudesert Park
> Henley-in-Arden
> November 23rd
> 1913

My dear Mummy
　　Have you got any stamps to send to me because I think that I shall begin to collect some in an album. Charley lost his voice for about 4 days and had rather a bad cold. This morning we went for a walk and had church here insted of the Village. We had the dancing just as usual and we are learning The Tango which is very nice and Interesting.

That last word with its capital 'I' reminds me that the tango could also be extremely funny. On our dancing nights the desks in the Big Schoolroom were shoved to one side by the bigger boys while we, the smaller ones, scattered French chalk over the boards and slid over them, as we slid over the icy pond in frosty weather, to give them a proper polish. The dancing was always better we felt (that is to say more enjoyable) when not incommoded by the presence of ladies: no hopes of a jolly good rough and tumble when *they* were on the floor. Why, we even had to wear cotton gloves! I suppose, otherwise, our sweaty or dirty hands might have sullied their ball dresses – certainly David's and Fabian's would have done so at once; and would George's or mine have been any cleaner?

We rose to our feet and bowed as Arthur Harry and She-Who-Must-Be-Obeyed entered the ballroom, and again as Mr Nathan, securely pinioned by Miss Whatley on one arm and by the dancing mistress on the other, was helplessly led into the torture chamber. We even shuffled uneasily about as Enid and Rosemary brought up the rear; though their supercilious stares were greeted with hostile grimaces and, from the bravest among us, with long noses. Safer not to – the little beasts were perfectly capable of sneaking. Miss Whatley went to the piano where Mr Nathan also stationed him-

self with a view to turning the pages for her. He could not, of course,
follow the score, but a violent nod of the head was enough to give
him his cue. He never complained about his lot, and may have welcomed it as he was not called upon to dance. Our instructress, who
also played the part of Mistress of the Ceremonies, suggested to
Miss Whatley and Mr Nathan that we should start with a onestep,
and then came the fatal words, 'Choose your partners, please.' This
was really pretty desperate, and in a way reminded one of musical
chairs – because the last two to pair off would be left with the girls.
Harry and Margery were no problem; though Margery might have
done as a partner we none of us fancied Harry, and they always
chose each other. The lady in charge did not disturb us much,
either. There was usually someone, temporarily in Harry's bad
books, ready to dance his way back into favour by selecting her as
a partner; or some sidey fool, like Jimmy, eager to show off; or,
again, a dutiful fool, temporarily head boy, who could hardly
escape the chore if he wanted to keep his uneasy crown; and, if all
else failed, she herself would deliberately choose the worst dancer
– which was, after all, part of her job – and quite often got landed
with Sooty or Val. As for the rest of us it was not so much a choice
of partner as a seizing of partner; and sooner than fall a prey to
either of the young ladies I have myself grappled with Horrie who,
for his sins, happened to be sitting next to me.

> Everybody's doing it, doing it, doing it,
> Everybody's doing it, doing what? The Turkey trot.
> See that rag-time couple over there,
> Watch their shoulders go up in the air,
> Oh my goodness, honey, I declare
> It's a bear, it's a bear, it's a bear. Where? There!
> Everybody's doing it, doing it, doing it,
> Everybody's doing it now.

Easy enough. All we had to do was march backwards or for-
wards in time to the music; though shoulders, as an extra refinement, could go up in the air at the right moment. In the middle of
each dance there was a dangerous pause, recognized, however, by
the authorities, which sometimes gave way to scuffles. It was
admitted that each partner should have his fair share of being the
gentleman; and on occasion the lady would administer a blow to
his gentleman if he was reluctant to change his sex. This particular

hazard was not run when dancing with the girls, but there were others far worse. For instance, we were supposed to engage them in conversation.

'Did you see the football match last Saturday?'

'No.'

'It was against the Wootton Scouts, and perfectly ripping.'

'Oh?'

'George and I scored two goals each, and we beat them seven-nil.'

'Oh?'

'Do you like dancing?'

'Yes, but not with you! Ha, ha!'

No wonder we did not like dancing with them; and it could never have entered our heads that one day we should. They made us feel so awkward that even the best among us forgot his steps and, what with frustration and annoyance, could hardly dance at all. Strange that, in a few years time, when for quite other reasons, it was still sometimes just as hard to make progress, at least over the boards, we readily excused the inconvenience they caused us since it promised a vigorous performance in another place. I don't think such a generalization would have applied to Jimmy at any age. He danced for the sake of dancing and might have preferred to dance alone; so that, spot-lit, leaping to the heavens in a series of complicated *entrechats*, his would be the sole glory of bringing the house down. That he did (or at least half of it) even at Beaudesert Park and, according to him, unintentionally.

He had (to the relief of Val and others) paired off with the dancing mistress for the next dance, that Interesting tango. For a time all went well. Heels clicked; arms writhed like serpents; curtsies were exchanged for bows, bows for curtsies; glides, as of crabs slinking over the ocean bed in parallel – all ended, as they were supposed to do, in a flurry of spinning, swirling skirts and stamping feet; and a sort of cloudy obscurity arose as when those crabs, at the approach of a hungry bass, frantically dig themselves into the sand. Indeed there was always something a little muted, a little sub-aqueous about the tango. It might allow more initiative than did the midnight minuet, but far less than the wild *fanfarron-adas* of the Andalusian gypsies as they fling about to sounds of castanets and the dry and thirsty whines of the flamenco. There was nothing primitive, nothing barbaric about the tango; nothing in the least childish. It did not throw sexuality at our heads, but delicately hinted in the most civilized way that more might well be expected to follow. It suggested that the sophisticated graces of a latin were, ultimately, to be preferred to the ruthless brutalities of a sheikh. As performed by Jimmy, however, many of these subtle refinements were lost; and although he and his partner could not be accused of anything indecorous it looked not so much like dancing as wrestling. I could only wonder who was going to win.

The tango was never really popular since it demanded a good deal of skill, and there were far too many movements to be learnt. In one of these, perhaps the climax to the whole, the gentleman advances directly on the lady and, poised as it were for the kill, holds her in a perilous arc quite Pisaesque in appearance but definitely less enduring. Our dancing mistress must have been dreaming of other triumphs to have relied on the muscular support of a weedy boy. A sudden long drawn out howl, as authentic a bray as can be heard these days in any of a thousand nightclubs from the Costa Brava to Cadiz, announced disaster. Jimmy stood his ground for a moment over his declining partner; but her weight, combined with the force of gravity, inevitably dragged him down, and the leaning tower collapsed. Had he managed at last to hack her? If so, then the victory might have been his, but battles are not always so easily decided as that famous one against the scouts of Wootton Wawen. In the end it turned out to be more of a draw than anything else.

Before the ref could intervene Max and I, not too close to be involved, were admirably placed to view the whole amazing spectacle. The next few couples, eyes on their feet and unaware of the accident ahead, sailed stately on and were sucked into the vortex; so that every time poor Jimmy seemed to be emerging from a maelstrom of rotating taffeta petticoats, he was shoved under again by more wreckage from above. His cries, less mellifluous than his partner's though very sweet and contagious, i'faith, gradually ceased as he preserved his breath for yet one more attempt to surface. He might never have emerged from under a pile-up, such as we are now used to on foggy nights on the motorways, had not Miss Whatley stopped playing and had not Mr Nathan, at the risk of his own life, gallantly erected a crash barrier. Now one of the victims was led out of the room by Margery while Sir, notebook in hand, was seen in earnest conversation with the other. But it was only later that we got at the truth of the matter. By the time order had been restored Jimmy was not to be found. What a rotter to have funked our enquiries and slunk away to bed! In this we did him an injustice. We could all see that he had been 'booked'. We did not realize he had also been 'sent off'.

When, at the normal hour, we went upstairs ourselves, he was put to the question. He indignantly denied he had hacked her. As he felt himself going he had simply put forward a foot in order to preserve his balance; and, since he could not see exactly where to put it, had unfortunately got his ankle entwined with one of his opponent's. Thus, exerting a little pressure to regain an upright position, he had brought off what was almost certainly an illegal tackle, a little mitigated since she had no right to cling on to him. We easily agreed with him that it was a rotten bit of bad luck. And when, at breakfast the next morning it was announced that every one of us would write out fifty times: 'English gentlemen do not laugh at the misfortunes of other people', we still did not blame him. Froggie, of course, foolishly took it into his head to argue that he was not an English gentleman and, on those grounds, should not be penalized. We could as easily have put forward the same plea. Sir coldly remarked he was doing his best to turn the baron de Lévis into one, and that he would write out that sentence one hundred times as a proof of it. Strange that for once, Sir could not see the joke. But not even Froggie found fault with the culprit. After all Jimmy was one of us.

> Present mirth hath present laughter:
> What's to come is still unsure.

While we never worshipped Arthur Harry, most of us and for most of the time looked upon him as a true hero. But there were two or three occasions when, in our view, he behaved in such an odd manner that we were forced to demote him to the lesser rank of schoolmaster. The first of these lapses was his reaction to that fatal tango.

There was plenty of time for recrimination and indignation, in the period after breakfast devoted to the two lavatories, to reach such a pitch that it was even suggested that we might withhold our labour and go on strike. The indictment reached unmanageable proportions since almost everyone contributed to it, but it was finally reduced to two main charges of 'unfairness' and of 'not seeing the funny side of it'. Sooty maintained that it was really a question of weight. Given a state of equilibrium the heavier body would inevitably drag down the lighter. The only difficulty was to determine the weight of the dancing mistress since Jimmy's (and ours) was recorded by Miss Whatley week by week. But that enquiry would have taken months of patient research and might never have been resolved; and action was immediately required. It was agreed, therefore, that in any disaster in which a grown-up and a boy was involved the grown-up was to blame as being automatically in charge of the situation, and further that an expert was more likely to preserve her balance than even a gifted amateur. Jimmy, therefore, an innocent victim, had been punished for a crime perpetrated by the dancing mistress. And what about the rest of us? Even those few couples who had been sucked down into the vortex had only done so because they had, under orders, been watching their steps and had no eyes for what lay ahead of them. Others, like Max and myself, were remote from the scene of action, and in no way committed. To include all of us in a general correction showed a cowardly weakness on the part of authority. It was as if Zeus, no longer sure of his aim in removing a particular offender from the scene with a thunderbolt, made sure of his prey by releasing on all mankind a plague or a flood from which none could hope to escape.

Val foolishly offered a sort of defence on behalf of his headmaster, which was instantly squashed by David.

'Well, we did all laugh, didn't we?'

'Who wouldn't?'

'Well, he seemed to think English gentlemen wouldn't.'

There were so many obvious replies to this argument and some not quite so obvious, that Val, stopping up his ears, retreated from the fray. But he had inadvertently turned our attention to the second charge. If somebody slips upon a banana skin, if a hat goes bowling along a street ineffectually pursued by its owner, the first reaction of the spectators is to laugh and they go on laughing while they help the victim to his feet or join in the chase for the hat. It is so instinctive that I very much doubt whether even English gentlemen, and in those days they were still to be found, could have refrained from laughing. That laughter is, of course, nervous and not at all malicious; but in considering the scene in later life I came to the conclusion that poor old Sir could not admit what it really was that disconcerted him, and diverted his own rude thoughts from the spectacle of the fallen lady to the rude laughter of the bystanders – a transference which could not have altogether satisfied him, as witness the severity of the sentence imposed on us.

We younger boys longed for direct action. How easy it would have been to upset inkpots; constantly to have asked 'to leave the room'; dropped books; blown noses; shuffled feet, and so on. But the elders, led by Val, Max, and Bobby decided that all such tricks would be playing into his hands. He was familiar with them and relished battle on those grounds. No, something more subtle was required. We were to show him that he no longer had our confidence; and, while behaving politely and correctly, that we were no longer chums. I, for one, felt sure that such a feeble way of showing disapproval was bound to fail, and that he would not even notice it. But he did. The atmosphere was sultry and gloomy in the big classroom; and it must be remembered that he was, to his great credit, at heart a softie. He asked 'What was the matter with us?' And received the unanimous reply, 'Nothing.' He referred to individuals as dying ducks in thunderstorms – always good for a laugh – but we did not even smile. When the morning break came he dismissed us with the words: 'If you think I don't know you're up to something, you maddening little animals, you're making a big mistake.'

In the playground we gathered in conspiratorial groups instead of rushing madly about, and poor Sir, forced to smoke a lonely pipe in the shrubbery, must have felt pretty wretched as he was always asked to join in, and on this occasion had not been invited.

'We've got him on the run,' said George. 'If we can only keep it up till lunch I'm sure he'll cave in.'

'He doesn't look happy,' said Val. 'Seems a shame. Perhaps we ought to let him off.'

'He is not letting me off when I was not possible ever to be that thing, an English gentleman.'

'Same here, Froggie,' said David. At which there was a good deal of laughter.

'Yes, but I get it twice in the neck, and you only once.'

'Because you argued, you ass,' said Max.

'And logically,' said Sooty, 'you might have had to write out those lines *ad infinitum* since, whatever else you might be, you're never going to be English.'

'Ha! No? You think not? If I want, my good Sooty, I only must apply in writing to the Home Secretary, and then I will be one like all of you.'

Luckily the bell now rang or we might have been discussing for ever the baron's chances of becoming English. Nothing relieved the monotony of those last hours before lunch. Harry fairly sweated to get matters back to normal, without any success. For that he required not our co-operation but our love, and we steadfastly withheld it; though Val was not the only one who felt sorry for him. He got more and more depressed, and looked so unlike himself that when we all trooped into lunch Margery asked him if he felt ill.

'No. A bit flummoxed. Trouble getting it into their thick heads about the French subjunctive and conditional tenses. Henri, of course, the exception – but then, just as I thought we were making a little progress, he informs me that they're looked upon as old-fashioned, and hardly ever used except by schoolmasters. I wish they'd make that clear in their grammars. Save a lot of time.'

At this moment he was called to the telephone; and when he came back he was as red in the face as before he had been pale.

'And what was all that about, dear? Butcher again?'

'I wish it had been – and the baker, and the candlestick-maker. It never rains but it pours. No, it was that damned – I mean it was Miss Seymour.'

'I hope she's quite recovered.'

'Sounded like it; sounded very lively indeed.'

'Well, that's something to be thankful for. No bones broken, and recovered her temper?'

'She said nothing about her bones, but her temper still seemed in a bad way. In fact, she has refused to come here again.'

'Don't forget, Harry, she's under contract, and her fees have been paid for the whole term. Are we to pay her for making a fool of herself? For simply collapsing and pulling Jimmy down with her? And what a ridiculous sight it was! I couldn't help laughing. I suppose she blamed the boy, but it obviously wasn't his fault. What do you think, Mr Nathan?'

'Well, every now and again you can't help a skid when the road's slippery. Probably too much chalk on the floor. I took it to be an accident of a minor nature, more like a slow puncture than a blown cylinder head. Just bad luck, really. All in the day's run.'

'Thank you, my dear, Thank you, Nathan. And I suppose I had better let these maddening little animals get it off their chests, as they've been bottling something up all the morning. Best to get it out into the open and then we shall see where we are. You, Henri.'

'If I might say so, Sir, I would have thought that Jimmy could not have been to blame as he would have been lesser than Miss Seymour. Also, in France, if anything might be pleasant, we would laugh with all of ourself, as you might do in England. Also, I say, as yet I am not the English gentleman.'

'All right, Sooty, what's bothering you?'

'He should have said "lighter", Sir. It's the weight that counts, not especially the size. If two bodies are circulating —'

'I get your meaning, Sooty. I think Miss Whatley has something to say.'

'Well, Mr Richardson, I can tell you Jimmy's just around seven stone.'

'Yes, but according to Sooty, Miss Seymour would have to weigh more; and how on earth are we going to get at that figure? Without it we should be at a loss for an equation.'

'Oh, there are ways of judging. I should say Miss Seymour was nearer nine stone than eight, wouldn't you Mrs Richardson?'

'I think you're being over-cautious, Miss Whatley. That fashionable balldress of hers, and all those taffeta petticoats, concealed a good deal of her person; but when she fell over enough was revealed —'

'Quite, my dear, quite. I take it, then, that whatever the exact weight of the lady might be, she would be heavier than Jimmy?'

'Without a doubt. Perhaps by as much as two stone, or even more.'

Harry began now to look more relaxed. He even managed to smile.

'Well, then, it seems I've put my foot in it on that score at least. I suppose, too, I shall be accused of being without a sense of humour. Miss Seymour was particularly upset by all that laughter. I was simply horrified myself. You found it funny, my dear?'

'Really, Harry, I ask you, who wouldn't?'

'Them's my sentiments, too, Sir.'

'David, my boy, it was not your sentiments we were discussing.'

'The school, Sir,' said Hippo, blushing, 'agrees with Mrs Richardson, it honestly was terribly funny.'

'I didn't think so, Sir. I felt as if I was drowning.'

'Thanks, Jimmy, for being on my side. I felt rather like that, too. Still, I'm not best pleased with myself. I can't think why I had to take it so much to heart – seem to have suffered a sort of blockage of all my senses. All the same I did snatch the boy from those – er, swirling – from without the whirlpool, so to speak. I suppose he was coming up for the third time. Oh, so you *can* laugh, you maddening little animals? Well, so can I, and I hope to contribute my mite to the general relaxed state of affairs by cancelling those lines – a waste of good fool's-cap anyhow, under the circumstances. Further, since we've all been in a condition of nervous tension this morning, I suggest we take a half-holiday this afternoon!'

We answered Val's request for three cheers for Mr and Mrs Richardson, Miss Whatley, and Mr Nathan with a full throated roar.

A narrow squeak, perhaps, but so be it. We were a closely knit little society and far from expert in dealing with awkward situations. So, when we were subjected to infiltration by foreign bodies we reacted in the accepted immunilogical fashion, and simply combined to expel them. We were not overawed by the refinements of Donnington Hall, nor were we much impressed by the casual conduct of the scouts of Wootton Wawen; and after a little hesitation we could take the loss of a dancing mistress in our stride. We were self-sufficient and went our own way happily enough.

Our gardens, ragged and dormant that autumn and winter, were now ready for planting; and thanks to Fabian very cheaply. When he suggested that trees could be grown from seed he did not look to the future. One square yard of Warwickshire soil however fertile would hardly produce to maturity a dozen forest trees; but to begin with they might economically take the place of a packet of sweet peas. These had been the rage last year, and had proved an expensive failure, throttled by a wild native plant *convolvulus eroticus britannicus* (better known as the gardener's curse, Bindweed.) Needless to say we were all keener on planting than weeding. In the playroom Fabian had set up a fine row of medicine bottles filled to the brim with water, and each held an acorn or a chestnut. When the first long white roots began to descend we were not slow to follow his example. But I, still I regret to say with a view to profit and not considering the wealth stored in timber, which would have

been a long-term view beyond my capacity and from which only
my heirs in any case would have been likely to benefit, decided to
try my luck with orange and apple pips.

After the annual digging of our gardens by Hopkins there was a
rush of planting. Crowds of tiny firs, oaks, beeches and chestnut
trees started off on the battle of life, but even so the gardens still
had large empty spaces, and as we had run out of seeds we were at a
loss how to fill them unless by purchase. Fabian solved this problem,
too. He instructed us to sink basins, pots and pans, anything that
would hold water, wherever we found room. The season of tadpoles
and tiddlers was upon us. As for the former it was well known that
frogs were the friends of gardeners, though incapable of weeding;
and the latter would destroy any mosquitoes which we might have
scooped up from the pond. Here again I deviated from the rest – in
company with one or two other gardeners blessed with original, or
exceptionally lazy, minds.

I saw, at once, that it was going to be an awful chore to stagger
back with a daily bucket of water from the pond half-way down
the drive. Pots and pans, especially discarded ones, are notoriously
given to leakage; and the whole point of an aquarium is that it
should contain water without which the inhabitants come to a
ghastly end. It struck me that a zoo would be more manageable.

The four corners of my allotment occupied by the trees left a
large area at least two foot square in which I planted a large biscuit
tin. I sunk it to ground level and it was covered with a lid which I
pierced with holes so that the occupant would not be able to escape
and at the same time would find it, I hoped, just like a home from
home: airy and dark. I covered the floor thickly with straw and in
one corner lodged a small trough for drinking water. Round this
dungeon I planted daisies. When I had finished my work I stood
back and saw that it was good. But I was a little worried by what
my neighbours had been up to. David had taken no trouble with
seeds or bottles. In the spring he had gone to Mother Nature herself,
and had transplanted half a dozen sturdy saplings which had a
start of at least four years on my laboratory growths, and threatened
to deprive them of light. He was not such a fool after all: his garden
would certainly not need weeding since weeds do not flourish in a
forest. Sooty, my other neighbour, had been less obvious but just as
skilful. *His* was very much of a rock garden. Not one square inch of
earth was visible. The first layer consisted of pebbles which he had

trodden firmly into the soil. On top of this solid foundation he had piled up a great pyramid of boulders out of which he expected confidently that flowers would grow of their own accord. My trouble here was that I thought it only too certain that the pyramid would collapse and crush my trees. Even a gardener's life, supposedly so peaceful and full of bliss, is not without its anxieties.

There was much to look forward to in the spring and summer of that fatal year of 1914. Margaret, under *force majeure*, had booked a passage home. Margery had sent an ultimatum to the effect that she 'would not be able to take the boys during the hols'; and my mother, who disliked nothing so much as having to plan anything in advance, was clearly check-mated. She had also been regularly bombarded by letters from me mostly pointing out that I had not seen her 'for years and years'. To add to the comfortable expectancy of the summer season I learnt that my father, too, was coming home. I imagine he had taken note of the European situation and wished to see his family if the worst came to the worst and made him an exile in India. Only one cloud threatened my summer: the zoo was still without a tenant. To go on a successful safari I should have to wait until Hopkins took *his* holiday and he seemed curiously reluctant that year to leave the boy in charge of his rose bushes. That would give me the opportunity I needed. The boy would have so much on his hands, mulching, spraying, attending to the borders and devastating every bush and plant in sight, that he would not have a moment to spare for the extermination of another and higher order of life at which he was just as expert – a life quietly and inoffensively going about its business in and around the stables.

At last, however, Hopkins withdrew from his labours and, impatient as ever, I hurried round to the stables. Pushing open the door I was met with a cloud of smoke, and there was the boy himself astride Mr Nathan's Indian and puffing a Woodbine. This was one of those confrontations which, at first sight, fill both parties with dismay; but after clarification of their respective positions can sometimes, I mean among reasonable and apolitical opponents, show room for manoeuvre and may even lead to a compromise satisfactory to both.

'Wot the 'ell you think you're up to?'

'Nothing much.'

'Didn't you 'ear Mr 'Opkins say as he wouldn't 'ave no damned kids around 'is stables? I've a mind to tell the boss on you.'

'All right. And how would you like it if I told Hopkins that the moment his back's turned you come round here to smoke a cigarette? And what's more I don't think Mr Nathan would like to hear about you riding his motor-bike.'

'I don't give a 'oot for Mr Nathan.' And to prove it he stubbed his cigarette out on the tank of that long-suffering vehicle. 'But, anyways, what *was* you up to?'

'Oh well, I just thought I might get a good mouse for my zoo – from one of your traps, I mean.'

'You might at that. Plenty to choose from.'

'If you like I could take over that part of your work until Hopkins comes back. Leave you more time to prune his rose bushes.'

'Too true. Still, if I lets you in on the mice, you'll 'ave to forget you ever saw me smoking in 'ere. And I won't say nothing to the boss about you getting your clothes filthy mucking about in the garridge when you oughter been playing ball with the other young gen'lemen. That suit you?'

'Yes, Thanks very much.'

'You don't 'ave to thank me. It's just a deal. But don't you forget it. For the next week you ain't seen me and I ain't seen you. After that if I catches you around 'ere I goes straight to Mr 'Opkins. Agreed?'

'Agreed.'

I went round those traps for a week releasing every indignant prisoner, being a little uncertain at first as to which would turn out to be a really good one; and thus assured the entire population, if it had had any sense, of at least a week's reprieve. But there was one criminal whom I found every day (not always in the same cell), so persistent in its preference for a life of confinement that I felt it would be entirely at ease in my tin. I transferred it without any trouble, and it immediately burrowed into the straw and vanished. But it learnt very quickly that the removal of the roof meant food and would come up from the depths to nibble at old stale bread or cheese rinds, and was so careless of company, or so greedy, that these tit-bits were devoured *in situ*; and I was always able to exchange a view of a minnow for a view of a mouse. We spent a good deal of our time in the gardens that summer as we attended not only our own but occasionally, and surreptitiously, our neighbours'. For instance I contemplated cutting down David's largest tree until he pointed out that I had better start to work on the rookery since, at mid-day, those enormous elms (still standing, and very splendid, I was glad to see on a recent visit) overshadowed all our gardens. He reminded me, too, that it was not unknown for animals to 'escape' from zoos; so I left his tree alone. Sooty was much more accommodating. If I wanted to remove the topmost pinnacles of his pyramid I was at liberty to do so on one condition – the labour was to be mine, not his. Sir, however, did not allow gardening to interfere with cricket. A bellow from the pitch would bring us scrambling over the railings from the delights of our gardens.

One evening I had been feeding my mouse – now so tame that it would sit in my hand and eat for all to see – when the usual shout reached us. I hurriedly put the creature back, fixed on the lid, and ran on to the field with the others. All went well until I was put on to bowl – unfortunately at Sir who was showing us the drive and the pull, calling for half-volleys and long hops, and thoroughly enjoying himself. But my very first ball gave him a nasty shock and he may well have thought that he was suddenly suffering from an attack of double vision. It is not considered sporting (and I believe I'm the only cricketer who has ever done so) to bowl two balls in the same delivery. One of them was a simple half-volley and bowled him because he had been concentrating on the other which had simultaneously been dislodged from my sleeve. This also looked harmless enough but as it reached the ground turned so abruptly on the turf that it became a leg break of extreme proportions and as it gathered speed up the slope and into the long grass I realized I had lost my mouse for ever.

In my early years I was much more tolerant of cold than heat; and towards the end of the summer term most of us were rather jaded. Fretful, languid, drowsy, apt to quarrel, uninterested in our work, we drooped and were clearly in need of refreshment. I think this must have been the origin of the second annual pilgrimage to the old wood, as Harry would wish our parents to see us in lively condition. It was a very different outing from the first. Now, in its maturity, the wood had become a forest, almost impenetrable. Brambles and bracken guarded its secrets and the rides were blocked. One only remained open to traffic; but that was enough, as it led straight to the pool in and out of which the day was spent. The pool was nicely graded in depth. At the far end the waterfall had dug out a basin just large enough for the grown-ups to swim in. At the other end where it trickled over and became once more the Little Alne we discarded our clothes and splashed about in the shallows; and were permitted to advance towards the exciting end, each strictly according to his size but none beyond his own tummy button. Mr Nathan, no bathing enthusiast, supervised this end of the pool, trousers turned up to the knee, ready for minor emergencies. The brothers Hopkins smoked silently on one side of the pool while the cook and her friend gossiped on the other. The boy, as usual rather betwixt and between and oddly clothed in a pair of grey pyjamas, held the centre of the stage more or less to himself and independent of anybody's jurisdiction – though he kept a wary eye on his Mr Hopkins who might wave a pipe at him if he bothered the swimmers or if he started a rough house by ducking any of us. Harry's dark blue combinations and the red skirts of the ladies added a shocking touch to the bright and sparkling scene. The ripples that splashed over our ankles from the deeper end brought with them the colours of the rainbow; and the land of happiness, as everybody knows, is only to be found where the rainbow ends – and where else, that peaceful afternoon, if not in the bountiful forest of Arden? But it is a never-never land for those who search for it with guides and maps. The earnest young man was on the wrong track, that vile afternoon, in the sad and sultry streets of Sarajevo. He was the first but not the last, in my lifetime, to lead forth a multitude into the desert of misery and death.

CHAPTER NINE

There were, as usual, surprises in store for us when we reached London to begin the summer holidays, but not quite on the same scale as those experienced when we had set forth on that Bedfordshire tour conducted by my father. In fact, he had little to do in the opening act of this new play and, after seeing us into a taxi, vanished underground to Belsize Park where Lady S. had installed herself after my grandfather's death. He was said to be going to join us later on at Frinton-on-Sea.

Margaret, from her point of view and careless as ever of international affairs, seemed to have made an admirable choice. 'Frinton-on-Sea' (to quote an old brochure) 'is rare among seaside resorts in south-east England in that it preserves a quiet, peaceful atmosphere so desirable to many people as a retreat from the hurly-burly of modern life.' She was not to know, nor would it have entered her head that Frinton might, at any moment, find itself in the front line.

We came, we saw, we fled. The Huns were always far more difficult to conquer, as even Caesar must have realized, than obscure tribes in Asia Minor, and the holiday mums, burdened with all their impedimenta, were obviously sensible in retreating. No one can blame them for that. But, personally, I hold it against them that they *all* chose to do so on the same day, and all by the same train; and it would not be much of an exaggeration to add, all by the same taxi. There was only one of these and Margaret had booked it overnight – but so had everybody else. We stopped all along the way for others to get in, much to Margaret's indignation which was not appeased by the driver's remark that, in times of war, we was all expected to muck in together. She pointed out that we were not yet at war and that, until we were, civil engagements should be honoured. This only infuriated him and he replied that we were free to get out and walk and he would make no charge although he had driven us at least a hundred yards towards the station. John and I took advantage of this offer thankfully at the next stop; where two women and three children somehow managed to squeeze in.

For the honour of old England I must make it absolutely clear that the retreat of two battalions of women and children from the fortress of Frinton showed no signs whatsoever of panic. We retired in good order and, so far as we visitors were concerned, the Germans, if they had sacked the place next day, would not have been richer by so much as a wooden spade. It was more like a mass migration of the peoples, quite common at this time of year in Europe, only in the opposite direction; and naturally such a phenomenon had not been anticipated by the Great Eastern Railway. If our tempers were not all that might have been desired it could be put down not to fear but to lack of transport; and soon enough irritability gave way to somnolence as one after another, at least in our compartment (which contained eighteen human beings), began to feel the effects of suffocation. It was a proof that we English, as a race not notably claustrophobic, are yet capable, if put to it, of enduring placidly conditions which only foreigners seem to enjoy. Margaret fought a drawn battle with an old gentleman who had the carriage to himself when it arrived at Frinton. She had forced him to put out his cigar but he had refused to open the window; and that's the last thing I remember about that dreadful journey until we emerged at Liverpool Street, and wonderfully, still alive.

My father, who had been summoned by telegram, was disconcerted by the irruption from our carriage of a crowd of pallid ghosts although he did his best to encourage us by enquiring if we had had a pleasant journey.

'Ralph, for goodness sake, quick before he goes, do you see that old gentleman making his way to the cab rank – the one smoking a cigar?'

'Yes, indeed. He offered his services? You would like me to thank him?'

'I would like you to take his name and address and report him to the station-master. He was smoking in a non-smokers' compartment.'

'Well, really, Margaret, at a time like this' – fumbling for pipe and pouch – 'I hardly think that would be very useful. I'd better get a porter. I'd have engaged one before if I'd thought there'd be such a crowd.'

He was let off that impossible task because Prodgers, always brilliantly prepared for any emergency, had leapt off the train and seized one of the few on duty. And he was thus spared an awkward encounter with the enemy who had escaped before my father was ready to pursue him. No doubt that old gentleman would have a sorry tale to tell in his club: a warning to his fellows of what they might expect to suffer if women ever got the vote.

During the luncheon interval Ralph produced a sheaf of telegrams that he had received from Margaret which required interpretation. Each contradicted the one before. 'LEAVING IMMEDIATELY ENGAGE MULHOLLAND HOVE.' 'LEAVING IMMEDIATELY MEET LIVERPOOL STREET 1230 PM.' 'LEAVING IMMEDIATELY TAKE APARTMENT BUGGERS HILL.' My father had decided that the second one was worth acting on though he now took the trouble to tell Margaret that to add the letters PM was a shocking waste of money as no train ever reached London from Frinton in the early hours.

'But what on earth did you mean by Buggers Hill? There ain't no sich place, my dear.'

'Well, there was a hopeless scrum in the Post Office and only one girl quite worked off her feet, poor thing, and rather a fool – but surely you might have guessed she meant Burgess Hill?'

'Never mind. Just tell me what *you* meant. Is it to be Hove or Burgess Hill?'

'Not Hove, with all these rumours about. I could not face another journey such as I've just had. I think further inland might be quieter, and Burgess Hill is bound to be healthy for the children as Doctor Dill himself has retired there.'

My mother was certainly very unlucky in choosing suitable places in which we were to spend those summer holidays. Burgess Hill had some advantages over Frinton. It was protected by the Downs and out of range from the guns of hit-and-run pocket battleships, but what none of us could have guessed was that the village, since the end of July had, judging by numbers, become a part of metropolitan Belgium. Many of those plucky little Belgians were also intelligent and had preferred the role of refugee in England to that of something worse than death at the hands of the enemy in their own land; and all available accommodation, as we cruised dispiritedly from agent to agent, seemed to have been taken over by them. Ralph began to refer to the place again as Buggers Hill, and sometimes as Brussels Sprouts Hill which cheered us up a bit; but as night descended he suggested we were refugees ourselves and might find a resting place, for the time being at least, with the Mulhollands. Hove was as likely as not to be quite empty, and too exposed, perhaps, to be patronized by Belgians. He emerged, however, from the last of the agents still open (business was booming in Burgess Hill) with an order to view the property of a Madame Lecointre in Ditchling Road. The agent admitted that a portion of the villa was already occupied, but believed there were still rooms to let. Only a week before his client had accepted a very nice Belgian family for an indefinite stay; and there was a friendly little chap who would welcome John and me as playmates. Dining-room, drawing-room, large well kept garden, view of Ditchling Beacon from front bedrooms, all mod-cons and a playmate.

'Really, Ralph, what about privacy? Did he mention that?'

'We might have to share the public rooms, but not the bedrooms.'

'And what sort of social life can be hoped for with foreigners and their dreadful manners? Think of them guzzling food with their knives.'

'He gave me to understand they came from one of the best families in Europe, if not the best – university people from Ghent – very acceptable, I'm sure. Besides, after all, Margaret, as things are – '

'I know what you're going to say, Daddy,' I shouted. 'In times of war we're all supposed to muck in together. We might not have to at dear old Hove. Can't we go to Hove?'

'I want to go to Hove.' John knew what mucking in meant.

'Hove,' bellowed Ursula.

'I reckon we should all make for Bedfordshire, wherever it may be, as soon as possible,' said Prodgers.

This little joke went down well and we were fortunate to find that county *chez* Madame Lecointre. She was still up and, used to dealing with refugees, gave us a warm welcome.

The next day the Germans invaded Belgium and on that fatal August 4th we declared war. I became, encouraged by blood-

thirsty reading and propaganda, as bloody-minded a patriot as anyone else, and all humanitarian cogitations vanished until the war
was over. At the very beginning – I think it must have been the
effect Aaland, our playmate, had on me – I was, indeed, a little uncertain where my sympathies lay. I did exclaim once, in a rage,
that I was on Kaiser Wilhelm's side as I knew he would have dealt
satisfactorily with Aaland whom I found an intolerable bore; but,
on second thoughts, I saw that I should not have had to suffer his
company if the Kaiser hadn't chased him overseas. For this disaster
the Kaiser was clearly to blame; and so my loyalties were fixed. I
agree that such patriotism as this was not especially highminded
but, stripped of resounding phrases, was the basic call to murder,
legalized and blessed by God's ministers in every warring country,
really much sweeter or nobler than mine? *Dulce et decorum est pro
patria mori.* Balls.

I was not of an age to appreciate the difficulties of refugees, and
the way Aaland introduced himself to me next morning in the
garden was far from courteous. I was bending over a hole in a bank,
where I thought I had seen something stir, when a sudden push
sent me rolling over. When I got to my feet I saw that a great, fat
lout had taken my position and was staring into the hole and
apparently gargling into it. I returned his greeting; and when he, in
his turn, had reached the levels of the lawn, I administered a couple
of telling blows to his bloated paunch. He was a little older and
much heavier than me but slower and softer. Battle was joined, but
ultimately only to John's advantage – neutrals always get the better
of it – who had for several minutes an uninterrupted view of the
hole and extracted from it a very splendid toad. Madame Lecointre,
deeply shocked, found us thus engaged; and at once gargling and
speaking English made us shake hands. She also had to judge whose
toad it was. John claimed it as his by right of capture, I that it was
mine as I was the first to spot it, Aaland with a forlorn and tearful
gargle that (as I understood from Madame) as a guest in foreign
parts he should be allowed to keep it as a pet. She had a better right,
I believe, than any of us to that toad but was generous enough not
to pursue it. We were to share it between us and John and I were
to teach Aaland English.

The main trouble with Aaland was that he had left his pet
rabbits behind him, and felt unhappy without them. The whole
family had made a dash for England and had only taken essentials

with them. Aaland fondly believed he would find these creatures
again on his return home; and John and I were decent enough not
to disillusion him, which we could easily have done by crude signs
if not by language. But when, at nightfall, that toad was unearthed
in Aaland's bed, we all saw the poor boy was in a really bad way,
and that something would have to be done about it. It was resolved
to advertise for an Angora rabbit. This suited the brothers well
enough as they would then have the toad all to themselves; and the
toad must have felt a measure of relief as it was returned to its more
natural habitat.

When the rabbit was finally located at a farm up on the Downs
it became my duty to help Aaland collect it since he was without
any known language and, though he was proficient on a bicycle,
had a fatal tendency to ride it on the right or wrong side of the
road. So one fine day, his handlebars sporting a sack, we wheeled off
to Pyecombe; and my spirits being buoyant I felt I might teach him
a bit of English by way of a song:

> Dick: It's a long way to Tipperary,
> It's a long way to go.
> It's a long way to Tipperary
> To the sweetest girl I know.
> Good-bye Piccadilly,
> Farewell Leicester Square.
> It's a long, long way to Tipperary
> But my heart's right there.
>
> Aaland: Phitz a phong, phong vy to Tippaphairy
> Phut my phart's vite tare.

I was obviously a born teacher.

I had been put in charge of the business arrangements by
Aaland's parents since he was as ignorant of our currency as of our
language, and they felt he was likely to be swindled. And so he was,
or rather they were, but not by the farmer's wife. She praised the
rabbit for its size and kindly disposition; and Aaland's explosive
remarks seemed to indicate that it was satisfactory. But I argued
that, though large enough, it looked pretty mouldy and was probably on the point of death. It might be worth two shillings but not
the half-crown with which I had been entrusted. After some debate
she accepted my offer and I found myself the richer by sixpence.
Aaland, seeing money change hands, seized the creature by the ears

– the accepted way of handling them – and transferred it to the sack but not before he had received a blow from its hind legs; which at least proved that it had a deal of life still to come, and it continued to thump about in the most spirited manner under confinement. We had to start off down a precipitous track, and as Aaland's hired bicycle (we English relished refugees) had defective brakes, I hoisted the load onto my handlebars and we set forth at a cautious pace. But not even my brakes were good enough to deal with the increased and awkwardly balanced weight; and there might have been a nasty accident if the animal had not, involuntarily, come to my rescue. Kicking wildly about inside the sack it had gradually sunk down and come to rest on the front tyre; and this was enough to get us safely to the levels of Pyecombe with the loss of only a small portion of fur. But there we all three required refreshment; and while Aaland appeased his rattled rabbit with a bunch of dandelion leaves I, never a miser, bought us two ice-cream sodas; and bang went sixpence. That rabbit's temper improved daily as long as we remained at Madame Lecointre's. It had a roomy hutch on her lawn (which it dug up whenever it had the chance) and a basket in Aaland's bedroom at the end of the day, though it was never found there in the morning. Our little playmate must have been tougher than we thought, for who else would willingly accept a mangy fierce old buck Angora rabbit with a redoubtable kick as a bed-fellow? Yet misery may acquaint us with stranger ones.

Between us we had managed to settle Aaland in a foreign land fairly comfortably and to his own satisfaction. But we ourselves were restless and discontented. It became clear quite early in those hols that Burgess Hill did not suit us. Margaret was never at ease with her hostess or fellow-guests, and never stopped grumbling. Ralph constantly slipped away to London; on urgent business, so he said. My mother was not to be taken in by such excuses, and was convinced that he was up to his usual tricks with the fiend Pippa – a state of affairs that always made her nervous. It was a relief, there-fore, when we received in his spidery handwriting an invitation to Dr Gordon Dill's ninety-second birthday tea party.

The doctor received us sitting in a large armchair clad in pyjamas and a chinese dressing-gown, many sizes too big for him. He had adorned his feet with red slippers; and a necklace, in the familiar shape of a stethoscope, hung negligently round his scrawny old neck – possibly as a warning to those who might dare to take liberties with him that his claws were still not blunt, possibly as a proud emblem of his long career, or more likely as a ready convenience in the frequent and all too necessary auscultation of his own heart. It is usual to give presents on people's birthdays and we were not without ours. Margaret presented him with a picture of herself – on horseback. He declared this to be a very good likeness. Prodgers had had much the same idea, only in her case she handed him a coloured print of the White House. Next Ursula came trotting forward with an object wrapped in many layers of paper. He gallantly set to work to strip this treasure of its mysteries – too much for Ursula's patience who helped him undo it.

'Why, if it isn't a doll!'

'Yes, it is. It's my new baby. But you can keep it as I've got others.'

John and I had been keenly interested in all this opening of presents, though we had long before seen them all; but after Ursula's had been admired we engaged in a bit of scuffling at the end of the room. It was not, on this occasion, anything to do with the rights of primogeniture (though, if I'd thought of it, I should certainly have put it forward as an additional reason for giving my present first). It was merely a question of classification. So far every gift had been for keeps. Now, my present was in a manner of speaking also for keeps; and John's was definitely not. Therefore, with a final shove, I advanced on the doctor with a large box.

'Many happy returns, Dr Dill. I think you'll find them fairly ripping.'

The doctor, who knew something about boys, ordered Tom to open the box and Tom, too, for the same reason, cautiously lifted the lid and nearly dropped the present when two very small frogs leapt out of it. The others were quiescent.

'Well, Dick, they *are* ripping. Thank you very much, but what am I to do with them?'

'Nothing. I'll put them in your garden and they'll eat all the harmful insects. Keep your roses going nicely.'

I delayed my departure as I felt that John's non-present might provide some amusement. He stood before the doctor struggling with a bulge in his shirt.

'I'm not actually giving you this, Dr Dill, as it's mine, but I thought it would be a treat for you just to see it.'

The toad was extracted at last and placed on the patient's knee not without a scream from Margaret.

'How many times have I told you, John, not to put that horrid creature next to your skin? You'll come out in warts.'

'That's so, ain't it, Doctor?'

'A very beautiful amphibian, Mrs Podmore, but I prefer the ophidia. The emblem of the snake has sustained me throughout my practice.'

'We were wondering about warts, Doctor.'

'Whats?'

'Warts!'

'Oh, warts. No, not on a healthy boy. Besides, it could act as a preservative against infection from fleas. Toads live on insects.'

'Mine's given them up. It only likes bread. I wish I could show you how it jumps, but it's stopped doing that, too. It was never much of a jumper, not more than about five inches at its best.'

He took out of his pocket a bit of bread, rolled it between his palms, as others nicely roll tobacco for home-made cigarettes, and held the pellet at a distance of three inches from his pet. The brute waddled forward, shot out a long tongue and wolfed down the tasty morsel.

'Sorry, but it's too lazy to jump. I might try holding a crumb above its head, just out of reach, and then it would have to jump or starve. I'll do that when I get back.'

'Yes, and that reminds me, Tom. Our guests will starve if we don't offer them a little refreshment. Bring in the cake.'

This was brought in with a flourish, and as cakes go was pretty good. But in one respect it did not come up to our expectations. There was only one candle on it and we had hoped for a multitude. He explained that he did not know exactly how old he was: somewhere, he thought, between ninety and a hundred and ten, and had settled for a hundred which could conveniently be represented by one candle – besides there wasn't room for more than about nineteen and he was sure he was older than that. Tom rolled back the doctor's sleeves; and although he bravely laid a trembling hand on the knife it was Tom who carried out the operation.

Later, when Tom appeared with a small glass of purplish liquid, Margaret thought it time to leave. I lingered on out of curiosity to see if Dr Dill was as good at taking medicine as I was.

'What on earth's this stuff, Tom?'

'Dr Hunter prescribed it, Sir, only this morning.'

'Poison, I dare say.'

'Yessir. But you agreed it might be beneficial.'

'Just to get rid of him. Here, chuck it down the sink and bring me a brandy.'

'Very good, Sir.'

My last sight of him was a cheerful one. He was relaxed, leaning back in his chair and drinking his own yellow medicine with evident pleasure. His head had sunk into his shoulders and he was now much more like a snake, or more accurately a slow-worm (since it was difficult to see where he began or where he ended), than any sort of batrachian with which John and I had pestered him: an old yellow worm sipping an old yellow drink; and about to slough his skin for the last time.

'Goodbye, Dr Dill. Thanks awfully for the party.'

There was no reply.

A few days later we left Burgess Hill for dear old Hove; and although none of us cared much for the Mulhollands their establishment was more spacious than that provided by Madame Lecointre. Ralph's task of fixing Margaret at Hove for the duration was made a little easier by her recent experiences at Frinton and Burgess Hill. She was persuaded that constant travel with children and baggage in suffocating conditions would only wear her out; and that a few months' residence in a house of her own until the wretched war was over might not be too disagreeable. But she was a slippery customer at the best of times and more than ever so when the opposition firmly believed she was bound hand and foot. Ralph conceded her terms which seemed reasonable – that under no circumstances would she return to our old house in Tisbury Road: a cold, damp house with sixty-two stairs from top to bottom. That she should positively discuss the matter at all seemed highly promising and this time Ralph hurried round to the nearest agents and even signed on the spot the lease of a house in Selborne Road. He was so keen to get a *fait* actually *accompli* that he did not bother to go over No. 11 himself at the time; and so he was lucky when in due course a more critical intelligence discovered that there were only fifty-six stairs, though the basement was declared to be as dark and as damp as that in our old home, and an ideal spot for the breeding of cockroaches. Nevertheless, Margaret seemed resigned to living there, and I was delighted.

During those holidays Ralph would sometimes take us for a

swim. Hove is not renowned for its long golden beaches but at very low tides a few yards of what might be called sand do appear; and the shore is generously provided with most formidable breakwaters behind which the populace can shelter from the south-west gales. My father did not look at his best in a swimming costume. I'm not at all sure that he could swim; and without his spectacles he was almost blind. But no one could doubt his courage and once, at least, it nearly brought him to a watery end and in a posture which had nothing of dignity to grace it. He had climbed out along a break-water, balanced on a distant pile, and plunged into the sea. The next moment he reappeared – or rather his feet did; and he waggled them about in such a highly comic way that I laughed heartily at this admirable piece of clowning. So, too, did a larger audience until one of its number noticed that the feet had become immobile and must have thought Ralph had stayed under quite long enough. He waded out to the exhibitionist and began to tug and heave at those pathetic feet; and at last my father emerged with a pop from the ocean bed and was assisted ashore. He had not been able to see that the depth of water was insufficient for a high dive and had simply got his head stuck into the sand. He might have broken his neck or drowned, and all I could do was to laugh. On being restored to us his first consideration was for others. We were not to mention this incident to Margaret. What a really decent chap my poor father was! I wish I could say as much for Margaret, but I have had to accept the fact that my mother was not a gentleman.

CHAPTER TEN

It was not until the very last night of the holidays that Margaret informed us that she had had the almost impossible task of deciding where she would be most needed. We, of course, including Ursula, would be perfectly secure at Beaudesert Park; but what might happen to poor Daddy, thousands of miles away in India, without her advice and companionship? I saw, then, what was coming. The old game was to be played all over again, and neither parents nor children were to win it. Prodgers took us to St Pancras and we arrived without incident at Beaudesert Park. My father might have been the joker in the pack, but my mother always seemed to hold the trumps.

There were changes even at Beaudesert Park, but I shall leave them aside to pursue my father's military career in India since it reached a climax before the year was out. En route to Calcutta, Margaret reported in a letter that she had seen lots of submarines, destroyers and battleships – including the *Emden*, on its way to harass our shipping in the Indian Ocean. If my mother had observed the *Emden* on the other side of the Great Bitter Lake we can be sure that more professional agents had spied it, too, and the authorities would have been warned in time that the Raj was threatened. At last the Calcutta Volunteers were to have a chance to show the stuff they and their cannons were made of. All that polishing and parading was, if only the Navy allowed the *Emden* to proceed on its course undetected, about to be rewarded. The Indian Ocean is very large and the Navy obliged, so that one day my father observed a blur of smoke on the distant rim of the Bay of Bengal. The ship from which it came approached the Hoogli in

a slow and devious manner and so cautiously that he suspected it
could not have been English. It seemed to zigzag about. With a
crisp word of command the battery was trained on the enemy. But
now a serious difficulty arose. How were those antique French
masterpieces to be fired? Since they had been removed from the
squares of Calcutta, which they had embellished for well over a
century, they had been loaded and unloaded constantly as part of
the drill. The commander-in-chief had, however, refused to allow
even a practice shot to be discharged for reasons which, to the
annoyance of the Volunteers, he kept to himself. So poor Daddy
was left with a responsibility which might have altered the whole
course of the war. He promptly decided to fire off what was an
almost virgin salvo at the enemy. But those seasoned veterans – I
mean the Volunteers, not the guns – were far from reckless.
Powder, in large doses, was laid against the breech of each gun; the
round shot rammed home; and nine trails of powder led back to
the firing point some twenty yards behind the battery where they
were all united. Ralph, having ordered his troops to ground in a
mangrove swamp still further to the rear, dropped a match on to
the pile of gunpowder at his feet and ran for dear life. Just as he
flung himself down with the others a tremendous explosion disturbed the siestas of hundreds of alligators for miles around and
obliterated in one glorious *feu d'artifice* the disgrace of ancient
capture and all tangible proof of it: an *amende* that even our sensi-
tive allies would have accepted as entirely *honorable*.

When, at last, the Volunteers advanced on the position they had
held for so long they found only an enormous hole in a sandbank.
It was resolved not to fill it in but to leave it as a memorial to the
French. After ordering the Last Post to be sounded my father dismissed the company to their civilian jobs. He went home himself to
prepare one of those reports that junior commanders find so difficult. He could perhaps claim that his battery had fired on the
enemy until the last gun had been put out of action; no need to
mention that all had gone at the same moment; and the Inspector-
General, if he took the trouble, might search every sandbank in the
area without finding a trace of them. He was feeling a little
relieved when to his surprise Margaret turned up later that night,
and although he must have realized fairly soon what had happened he got through that ordeal, too, with flying colours. She was
full of the excitements of the voyage, made some reservations on the

ship's lighting, regretted that there was no dancing on deck for instance, and complained that the trip took several days longer than usual.

'You see, we had to zigzag about.'

'Zigzag? Good gracious! Did you say *zigzag*? Heavens above!'

'Yes, just to put those submarines off their aim. I did point out to Captain Johnson as we entered the Hoogli, that surely the Bay of Bengal was safe enough; but he preferred to take no risks.'

'I think he was right. The Bay of Bengal is never safe. Still something tells me you were lucky. Yes, very lucky.'

'And then the best thing of all happened: as we steamed into port we received a salute from one of our own batteries. I suppose in recognition of our having arrived after such a dangerous passage. Captain Johnson told me he thought it was a nine-gun salvo, and ran up the Flag by way of acknowledgement. I felt very proud to be English, I can tell you. We always seem to do things in style.'

'In style, did you say? Well, yes, we do our best. I hope the battery commander doesn't get a reprimand for exceeding his duties. Jolly decent of him to give an old P. and O. a salute reserved for the Viceroy – or more likely the *Emden*. Talk about luck! Good Heavens! After all those narrow squeaks of yours – of ours I might say – I think we should celebrate this very fortunate re-union with a bottle of champagne.'

'And to whom shall we drink?'

'No question about that, my dear. *A la nation la plus éblouissante, la plus éclatante du monde entier! Aux français! Vive la France!*'

Such an explosive toast to our gallant allies must have relieved my father's pent-up feelings. Margaret thought the champagne had gone to his head. In telling me this story Ralph made me promise not to let the cat out of the bag, so my mother never knew the full extent, or the nature, of the perils she had, by a miracle, survived. But if my readers think that Margaret would have held it against Ralph they would be wide of the mark. It would have amused her enormously. On the other hand we should never have heard the end of it. It was always difficult to strike a balance between the best of my mother and the worst; and as a general rule we were prepared to sacrifice the best if we could avoid the worst. Ralph's reluctance to disclose to Margaret the dubious part he had played in this Indian saga was a proof that, on occasion, his discretion could match his valour.

Back at school, with Miss Whatley at the piano, we sang patriotic songs, such as:

> Don't cry-e
> Don't sigh-e
> There's a silver lining in the sky-e
> Cheerio, chin, chin,   (We don't give a fuck
> Goodbye, old thing   or   For old Von Kluck)
> Na poo, toodle-oo
> Goodbye-e

and:

> We don't want to lose you,
> But we think you ought to go;
> For your King and your country
> Both need you so.

I'm sorry to have to report that Mr Nathan was not immune to this fatal anthem, especially as it was too plainly directed by Miss Whatley at the only person of military age at Beaudesert Park. He and his machine went. They enlisted in the Motor-Cycle Corps, and I never heard anything more of him or of it.

Mr Hynd – the first replacement for Mr Nathan – hardly survived the autumn term. I think he went before it ended. From our point of view there seemed to be everything wrong with him. He was a foreigner, he introduced foreign methods of instruction (relying for their effect on ear pulling; among others, John's), he walked too fast and cursed us if we failed to keep up with him, took no interest in any kind of game, constantly reported us to Sir for the slightest misdemeanour, and (if all this was not enough) turned out to be a German spy. It was careless talk by Sooty that led to his exposure. Sooty had noticed that the number of goods trains and wagons had enormously increased, and suggested that munitions were being sent down from Birmingham, via Reading, direct to Southampton for transhipment overseas. Mr Hynd's ears had not been damaged. The very same evening, as soon as school was over, he was observed strolling up and down in the Railway Field. It was not, of course, out of bounds for him; but why go there at dusk and in a rain-storm? For a bit of fresh air? For a view of the Jungfrau? No, he had obviously gone there to count the number of munitions trains and send a message in code to Germany. I now formed a small counter-espionage committee. It consisted of George, Sooty and me. If we had kept quiet we might have escaped detection. But others noticed our conspiratorial signs and whispers, and we were gradually compelled to expand the Secret Service Corps until it included almost everybody in the school. We had enough recruits to keep Herr Hynd under constant surveillance; but too many for him not to be aware that he was suspect. Indeed, Roby (forgiven because under torture at the time) made it perfectly clear by blurting out: 'I'd sooner have my ears twisted off than be hanged as a German spy, Mr Hynd!' He, now fully aware that any further work for the Fatherland was at an end and that his very life was in danger, took the bold step of complaining to Mr Richardson. Sir, armed with various documents, called us together in the Big Schoolroom.

'Well, which of you maddening little animals have been spreading rumours that Mr Hynd is a German spy? Stand up.'

It was a blow to him when three of his favourites rose to their feet.

'I'll bet you weren't the only ones. Come along, any more?'

Everybody stood up.

'I thought so. Boobies, that's what you are. Not likely to pass even the Common Entrance Exam, let alone get a scholarship. Never heard of Switzerland, I take it? Never heard that the Swiss are neutral? Well, what about it?'

'He was always going off into the Railway Field and counting the ammo wagons on their way to France, Sir.'

'Well, if that makes him a spy, you might just as easily be one yourself, Sooty. Don't you count them, too?'

'He can't speak English, Sir. Not even as well as Froggie.'

'So all that does, my good Dick, is to make Froggie a spy, too, according to your logic.'

'I am not the spy, Sir. I am the chief ally. *Vive la France!*'

'Of course, I know all about that, Froggie. It was only Dick who thought you were a spy.'

'Sometimes, Sir, we heard him speaking German.'

'Very interesting, George. May I ask if you can speak German?'

'No, I can't, Sir.'

'Right. Then how did you know it was German?'

'Sounded like it, Sir.'

'Sounded like it! Do any of you bright specimens know what language the Switzers of Switzerland do speak?'

'Why, Swiss, of course, Sir,' we all shouted, laughing. How could Sir be so silly?

'That's just what I expected you to say. Well, they don't, as it happens. They have no national language.'

'Then Mr Hynd can't be Swiss. He's not dumb like them. He can talk, Sir.'

'Stale news, Val. He'd hardly be teaching you if he couldn't talk. The reason why all your arguments fall down is because, so to speak, they talk too much. Has no one ever told you that there are German-speaking Swiss, French-speaking Swiss and even Italian-speaking Swiss?'

'Mr Hynd speaks English after a fashion. So are there also English-speaking Swiss, Sir?'

'There are a few, but English is not among their native languages.'

'Well, Sir, you do see, don't you, that with all those languages they must make the best spies on earth? They could pass themselves off as Italians in Italy, English in England, Germans in Germany and French in France.'

'And no doubt as Hottentots in Hottentotland?'

'You're joking, Sir. But they might try it on.'

'In France we do not have Swiss spies. We shoot them all.'

'Good old Froggie. And we hang them over here, Sir, don't we?'

'We're not going to hang Mr Hynd, Dick. You three, that's to say if you're capable of understanding anything, take a look at Mr Hynd's passport.'

We looked at it and shook our heads.

'I suppose you can read this stamp? Stamped by the Foreign Office and perfectly valid. They're not likely to give a licence to spies to enter this country, are they?'

We were rather at a loss until Val, as head of the school, came to our rescue.

'There were other things besides spying, Sir.'

'Such as?'

'Well, Sir, we don't like sneaking.'

'Oh, come on, Val. Since we're having one of our inquests, you'd better get it off your chest. Otherwise we'll never get to the end of this wretched affair.'

'Have you noticed David's ears, Sir?'

'David's? Why should I? Dirtier than usual?'

'Don't they seem to you to stick out a bit sideways?'

'Nothing peculiar about that. Always did.'

'Well, what about mine, Sir?'

'Ditto. Flourishing, I should call them.'

'And Little John's?'

'Oh, good heavens, what am I to say about Little John's?'

'Do they seem to you level?'

'Quite frankly, Val, to my eye I can't see anything wrong with them.'

'And what about Roby's?'

'Look here, my boy, have I got to inspect everybody's ears this morning? I'm not an ear specialist, only a long-suffering headmaster.'

'Yes, Sir. No, Sir. I meant Roby's right ear. His left one's not too bad.'

'Thank goodness for that, anyway. What's the matter with his right ear?'

'It's going down a bit now, Sir, but you should have seen it yesterday.'

'Somebody give him a clip over it?'

'Not a clip; much worse than that.'

'Just a moment, Val. I know you're very thorough, but I think I've got your point by now. I should say it was something to do with people's ears. Couldn't we concentrate on just one ear? Am I expected to look at *all* your ears. It would take me years.' (Laughter.)

'Well, Sir, would Roby's right ear do?'

'That's up to you, Hippo, my boy. So far as I'm concerned you have a free choice. They all look alike to my eye, but select any single ear and keep to it.'

'I'll stick to Roby's then, Sir, as we were talking about it just now. He had to take it to Miss Whatley yesterday.'

'Spendid! That means we'll have some positive evidence at last. Will one of you ask Miss Whatley if she'll be so good as to spare me a moment in here?'

Miss Whatley appeared.

'Ah, Miss Whatley, sorry to bother you, but I understand Roby

took one of his ears to you for examination. Can you be so kind as
to give us any details?'

'Yes, he brought me his right ear. It was inflamed and swollen;
but I thought a little ointment might bring it back to normal. I was
going to watch it for twenty-four hours; and then, if it got no
better, I should have called in Dr Agar.'

'Good gracious me, Dr Agar! As bad as all that! We've been
very lucky so far this term. Val says the whole school's got bad ears.
It couldn't be an epidemic, could it?'

'In a way that's just what it is, Mr Richardson. I blame myself
for not reporting it sooner.'

'Oh well, then, I suppose we've got to send for Agar. What a
colossal bore!'

'It's not the sort of epidemic the doctor could cure. But *you*
could, easily enough. I thought I could spare you the trouble, but
he wouldn't listen to me. I call it a wicked shame.'

'Now, Miss Whatley, could you be a little more explicit? Hippo
has so confused me that I'm afraid I'm not very bright this morning.'

Miss Whatley gave us a defiant look.

'They don't like what they call sneaking –'

'Yes, Val said something about that.'

'You see, Mr Richardson, they tell me everything; and I'm
sorry to have to say they're getting twisted.'

'The boys are getting twisted. Yes, I've got that.'

'No, not the boys. Their ears.'

'Ah! you rascals, that's a mean thing to do, and stupid and
dangerous, too. You have heard Miss Whatley say that even Dr
Agar might not be able to deal with it. Supposing he had to call
in a specialist? Your parents would like that, wouldn't they?'

'It's not as bad as all that, Mr Richardson, and I did say you
could manage it yourself. They're not pulling each other's ears. It's
Mr Hynd's –'

'That's got nothing to do with me. Mr Hynd can look after his
own ears, or he can go to Agar if he wants to.'

'Mr Hynd is pulling their ears, and twisting them, Mr Richardson.'

'You see, Sir, it's Mr Hynd's way of teaching us.'

'When we forget, Sir.'

'And when we don't forget, Sir.'

'It's all the time, Sir.'

'Mr Hynd, it's Mr Hynd, Mr Hynd!'

'Well, we've unearthed a lot this morning. Thank you, Miss Whatley, for making matters plain. A most disagreeable affair. I can't think why Nathan had to leave us in the lurch. You three boys will go to Mr Hynd and apologize for your nonsense – and I mean apologize. He is not a German spy and you are supposed to be English gentlemen. Whatever other business remains to be settled does not concern you.'

After a decent interval, during which other business must have been settled, Hopkins the Hearse appeared early one morning and Mr Hynd was carried off out of our lives for ever. At the beginning of the next term, in the same way, we received Mr Heglar. It looked as if history was about to repeat itself – which, after all, is what it does – because Mr Heglar was every bit as German as Mr Hynd and, given a chance, would have made as good a spy. However, no doubt through the good offices of our headmaster, a compromise was reached. Swiss and English came to terms satisfactory to both parties: no ear-pulling, no spy-baiting.

By the spring holidays the dream that was No. 11 Selborne Road *did* materialize. It was Pippa who became the first head of state and who welcomed us on our arrival. (Margaret, on her way back to us from India, was delayed by submarines.)

This was the beginning of my long intimacy with Pippa; and she was for much of my life a true friend and adviser and at all times a fascinating raconteuse. But she was, by nature, far too reasonable ever to conform to the pattern that would have numbered her among my girls. She was never quite able to allow her instincts a fair go, never resorted to inexplicable caprices, never took refuge in alluring flights (except of fancy); and never surrendered to the normal sexual pleasures though at one time hard pressed by Roger Fry. To say that she was a sympathetic companion is not to belittle that state since everybody welcomes comfort; and she bestowed it on everybody if they required it. As an example of this benevolence I can mention the case of the Greek Orthodox Church which attached itself to her in Constantinople and was escorted by her to London. Its representative's trouble had to do with a large parcel of salami, which was to support him for a month in foreign parts;

and, although without a common language, his fear of the con-
fiscation of this supply en route was quite clear to her. Sometimes
he would hide it beneath his cassock, sometimes she would sit on it;
and so between them they smuggled the precious cargo past half
a dozen customs posts and brought it safely to Victoria and none
the worse for wear. It never entered her head that it might not have
been excisable; and out of pure kindness of heart for a frightened
stranger she had taken the risk of a deal of unpleasantness if not a
heavy fine. And as if this were not enough she yielded to his request
for a loan at the last barrier of all; and to my amazement, and to
the honour of the priesthood, the loan (with a slice of salami, by
way of interest) was repaid the very next day. No part of this
adventure nor its happy ending caused her the least astonishment.
I can vouch for the grand finale of this story as I happened to be
present and partook – the right word to use, I think, since the meal
had sacramental connotations – of the salami laid on crumpets,
and observed the repayment of borrowed monies. It was not a
brilliant social occasion but bows, smiles, and exclamations of
'Very good' carried us along in an orthodox manner until the guest
departed. We were then able to relax and she told me the whole
story punctuated by her high wild screeches of laughter. We
speculated as to what provisions the reverend gentleman would
take with him on the return journey. Pippa suggested, sensibly
enough, that he would have no difficulty in buying any amount of
salami in Greek Street; but I, always in favour of variety, wondered if he might not invest in kippers: just as tasty if they survived
the journey. Of course, as she pointed out, he would have been
very lucky to have found another English lady willing to hatch
them.

In all such matters Pippa was unusually free and easy, and one
might have supposed that the conventions would not have inhib-
ited her in relationships of a deeper nature. It was something else,
or perhaps a number of factors combined, which proved insuper-
able to an affair with Roger. In many ways they were obviously
suited to each other. They had in common much the same background, sterile on the emotional side, fruitful intellectually; but
while he had escaped from the rigours of a puritanical upbringing
she had remained confined within the limits of theoretical liberty,
and seemed unable to break those bonds and put freedom to the
test. Roger's wife had, now and then, on the score of insanity, to be

removed from his life and I can understand his need for a more permanent relationship – and yet, more than once, he had fallen in love with women who had subsequently gone mad on him. That seemed to be his pattern. There might have been something in him that sent them mad but I think it was likely that he sniffed out the touch of madness in them, and fell madly for it. One of these, on the plea that he was in need of a rest cure, he pursued even within the walls of the asylum in Brussels where she was being treated, and indeed, underwent some sort of treatment himself; but since there is no known cure for love he was discharged after a few days, reluctantly leaving his loved one behind. With regard to Pippa he must have been encouraged, in the first instance, by the extraordinary adventures and people she encountered every day, and could only have felt an overwhelming desire to take a share in them. But though she may have been a tasty morsel for the unbalanced which they could not resist, he soon found out that hardly anyone was more completely sane than Pippa. In those circles there were plenty of others with whom he could find consolation of the sort he fancied, and Vanessa Bell was among them if only temporarily. In his last years, by dint of perseverance and good luck, he discovered his ideal mate in Helen Anrep, mad enough to keep him lively but never so mad as to be put away; and he may be said to have lived happily ever after. Pippa's fate was not so simple. She was never to meet a man so much to her taste as my father but her relations with women were almost always deep and lasting; and although she might not have acknowledged all the implications of this preference for her own sex, it brought her an ultimate satisfaction beyond even that experienced by being the leading figure on so many committees, and greater even than the resulting triumphs of her struggles for women's rights.

I have celebrated my first real meeting with Pippa by means of digressions but there is no need to excuse them as I was naturally led on to thoughts of later intimacies with such an important person in my life. She it was who told me a story about my grandfather and a bear. It was on a narrow ledge in the Pyrenees that they came face to face. Although both parties were on the small side so was the ledge; and there was not the slightest hope that either could pass without inconvenience to the other – and more likely that both would end up at the bottom of a precipice. Since my grandfather was also on all fours the bear may have mistaken him for a friend. After a long silent pause the General opened the conversation with a mild 'Shoo!' to which the bear replied with an equally gentle 'Whoof!' And at last, coming to the conclusion that his friend might have got stuck, very graciously and cautiously turned on his tracks and retreated, allowing Sir Richard to proceed on his way. A nice little story with a happy ending.

Dear old Mums, having made light of battleships, batteries, and submarines, was appalled by what she discovered at No. 11. For a few days, however, while she was reviewing the situation, we continued with our accustomed tasks; and she herself undertook the shopping, accompanied by either John or me to carry back the supplies.

On one of these expeditions an event occurred that some have thought had a bearing on my career as a writer, at least as a writer of children's books; and although it might have acted in the manner of a spring which releases the jack-in-the-box I must warn the literary critic in search of sources not to follow any such false scents. A work of art is not the product of catalysis. There is already, from the beginning of time, some mysterious factor within the foetus, some unconscious yet irresistible urge, unrelated to the normal processes of growth, which seeks for expression; and sooner or later it will make itself manifest in one form or another. Incidentally and paradoxically the less an artist depends on reality the more likely he is to achieve it: as if he is able to reveal more of what he sees and feels, and therefore more of what is to be seen and felt, by observing the phenomena of life out of the corner of his eye rather than by any photographic vision or reportage. It follows that a work of art, to be effective, cannot rely on its content. It is the style alone that gives it value. The Madonna and Child, as a subject a great favourite with the early painters, is tiresome if regarded, as it too often is, from the appeal to the senses. The emotional approach is barren and superficial. But some few of these works we return to again and again because of the *way* they have been painted. An impression has been created, a sight of unsuspected depths, something of greater significance than the everyday world has to offer us and far surpassing it in power and truth. This reinforced and almost magical effect is achieved by few and simply cannot be manufactured. Since I believe that the most important contribution to civilized life is made by artists, and would wish to encourage and preserve them, it is distressing to reflect that they are born not made. Might we not do more than is customary to cherish these illustrious births?

It is high time I returned to a less exalted level. One day Margaret and I were in a fishmonger's, patiently awaiting our turn, with a fine specimen of a plaice as our objective. But at the very moment when the choice was ours a large woman of indeterminable race seized the fish in her bare hands and triumphantly carried it off with her. My mother's protests were disregarded and we had to put up with an inferior member of the same species. I looked upon this lady's initiative as an example to be followed in the future: not to hang about in a genteel fashion but to clasp the article to one's bosom and make off with it. We were obviously behind the times. Margaret fulminated all the way home. She was convinced the woman was a Jewess since only such would steal food from the mouths of little children, and I gathered that one, Rachel Costelloe, better known to me as Aunt Ray, given the slightest chance, would have behaved in the same way. I thought Margaret should have been a bit more sporting about it, was ashamed of the fuss she had made in the shop, and bored stiff by the first of many diatribes against the Chosen People. And so it came about that, more as a joke than as a lesson in tolerance, that evening's bedtime story to Ursula (one of my more useful jobs as she would not go to sleep without one) introduced a new hero who, though his adventures were typically English, at least had a Jewish name. Night after night my mother had to listen to the opening paragraph, a theme song as it were, without which Ursula would not listen to the story that followed.

> Once upon a time there was a little boy called Little Reuben, and he had a sister called Little Rachel. Their father was called old Mr Isaacs, and they had a nurse called old Rebecca who looked after them.

There! No mother, the whole family as Jewish as I could make them, and the little girl blessed with the name of Rachel: a bitter draught for Margaret to swallow, but surely she deserved it for being such an ass about Jews? So, if it's of any interest to anyone Little Reuben was conceived of a fish, announced to Ursula in one war, gestated for years and years and was finally ready to be born during the next one.

After our distressing encounter at the fishmonger's Margaret felt she was not strong enough to face the horrors lying in wait for her at the shops. Unfortunately Prodgers, who was so firm with merchants and stood no nonsense from her fellow customers, was as weak as a worm with Ursula; and worse still could not be better employed. She spoilt her dreadfully. The scenes especially at breakfast (which my mother did not attend) were so loud and prolonged that even John and I used to a good deal of din as we were, and possibly attracted by it – as the melancholy litany of a jackass with its gradually increasing tempo and dying fall will inspire an anthem from lugubrious friends for miles around – could not resist also braying each after his own fashion. We said it with music. John was in charge of this department, an ancient and far from mechanically perfect gramophone, with a repertoire of classical and light comedy records some of which were 'grooved' and others cracked. Further, to get the side of one of these records *in toto*, it was necessary for the conductor to wind up the machine half-way through. Should that be neglected, and it often was, the effect was an almost perfect representation of a rallentando achieved, as above, in nature; and if the needle, caught in a deep canyon, were not given a sharp push the endless repetition of a few bars from the *Tales of Hoffman* was enough to send even a music mistress mad. His favourite was the '1812' overture; but above all that thumping and banging and blaring I had to raise my voice as I read to the company select passages from *The Anatomy Of Melancholy*, 'Hudibras', or *The Advancement Of Learning* – books my father had forgotten, probably on purpose, to take with him to India. We did everything in our power to educate our audience.

Margaret could hardly fail to hear this uproar and one day came down to the dining-room to see what was going on. She found Ursula, quite capable of feeding herself, being spoon-fed by Prodgers. It was not as if the poor old thing simply had to dip a spoon into the porridge and shove it down Ursula's throat. Although the porridge, once decanted into each bowl, could be garnished with milk, cream and sugar according to personal taste, this mixture appeared to be too gross for our fastidious young gourmet. Each separate spoonful had to be adorned first with a drop of milk, then a dollop of cream, and finally coated over with brown sugar; and not until all that had been done would she condescend to swallow it. It was at this time I came to the conclusion that babies were far more trouble than they were worth – rather

late in life but better late than never. Margaret found us engaged
in what seemed to be a riot: Ursula screaming at Prodgers, John
and I yelling at Ursula, the gramophone grinding away and
Prodgers grimly balancing a spoon that nevertheless often ended
up underneath the table.

'Ussella, Ussella dear, all ready for you now. That's a good girl.'

'Why don't you let her starve?' I shouted.

'Let her eat it up off the floor,' John yelled. 'That would teach
her.'

A scene such as this finally persuaded Margaret that Prodger's
skills were being wasted. It was as if a racehorse had been attached
to a plough. She hurried upstairs to her writing desk and within a
couple of days a healthy young woman from the Norland Institute
(whose name I never knew, as she was always addressed as Nurse)
descended upon us. Order was restored; and oddly enough without
the slightest protest from Ursula.

John and I, though pleased with the spaciousness of the basement at No. 11, came to the conclusion that, in spite of the bicycles
and the two playboxes, it was a little bare. It had been a good year,
at Beaudesert, for tadpoles and tiddlers and under that impression
I was keen to start a salt-water aquarium and he, for his part,
thought that we might run a zoo at the same time. A couple of cats,
or rather kittens, would do for a start; and taking Margaret by surprise we extracted from her the necessary permission. She might
have thought that, so far as the kittens were concerned, other forms
of life which had always been too evident in the basement might
be kept under control; and anything in a tank was likely to stay
there.

So, with half a sovereign in our pockets, we set off to furnish our
room. We did not have to search long for pet shops, but the goods
they offered were not to our taste and quite beyond our means.
After a fruitless morning I suggested that we might go off to the
Lanes in Brighton after lunch, since, here and there, the dealers in
fine art had not been able to eliminate purveyors of altogether less
exquisite objects. At last we came to one dealer whose turnover
that day must have been negligible, as, after the usual misunderstandings and arguments, we got him to listen to us.

'Wot you want a aquarium for? There's one down the road
good enough for most of us. You pays your sixpence and you can
watch that there shark till they turns you out. Also, starfish. But

if you *must* 'ave one all to yourselves, I got the very thing. This 'ere
goldfish bowl is the largest in the Lanes. Why, there ain't another
like it in all Brighton! Mind you, I'll be frank with you. It won't
take a shark but a couple of fair-sized crabs 'd get in easy; and I'm
selling it cheap too.'

'But, with that crack down the side, will it hold water?'

'Crack? Who's talking about a crack? That's just a fault in the
glass, and I'm selling it as a bargain.'

He took it to the front window, muttered to himself, walked
through the shop to the backyard, and hurled it into a corner. Its
arrival startled a cat and a covey of kittens into the open. I caught
a glimpse of a number of large glass receptacles, neatly stacked.

'Some folk is mighty 'ard to please.'

'Would you mind if we had a look round your yard? I think I
saw something there that would suit us.'

'You're welcome. As I told them police, only last week, you're
welcome as you won't find nothing but junk there. But I ain't got a
better way of spending me afternoon than a-waiting on you 'and
and foot, so let's 'ave a look, shall us?'

'Those tanks are about the right size.'

'Well, why didn't you say tanks to begin with? Them's not
aquariums, just ordinary acid containers. I 'as an agreement with
the Council over them tanks, but I dare say I could sell one to the
public if they was prepared to pay for it.'

'I say, you've got a lot of kittens.'

'It's that damned cat – always 'aving them. Worse than junk;
the Council don't want 'em and nor do I – that's to say, one or two
of them in this lot is particular 'andsome, so I ain't a-drowned 'em
yet. I might consider a sale to a kind owner with a good 'ome, I
might. But some kittens is worth their weight in gold. You don't
give 'em away for free, I can tell you.'

It was hot in the yard and the proprietor soon retired into his
shop. The cat had got under a bit of old iron with most of its brood.
Two, however, were engaged in some mild sparring outside, with
tails (such tails as, at that tender age, they were equipped with)
wagging furiously in the dust; and they were already sufficiently
advanced to be able to paralyse each other simply by staring – a
means of battle evolved only by cats and economical of blood,
sweat and fur. They seemed to us to have nothing wrong with
them, and we put them on one side into a tank to cool off. It was

much more difficult to decide on a choice of aquarium. Some were chipped at the top edges, others with glass too thick to see through or too deeply coloured. We went over most of that pile, laboriously re-stacking it, until at last we found one without blemish. And then came the reckoning.

'Well, I'll say this much for you: you've got eyes for a good cat when you sees one. These two are the best of the bunch, and I was a-going to keep 'em myself whatever I did with the others. Both males, so they won't cause you no trouble. As for that partic'lar container I'd made up my mind to charge the Council double for that one. It's a real beauty and no mistake. You don't expect first class goods for nothing, do you?'

'No, but people are often glad to give away ordinary kittens. These aren't Persian or anything. They're just plain English.'

'I see you've still got something to learn, son, about cats. An English cat is the best in the whole wide world; and as for your Persians and so on you'll 'ave to spend your lives a-combing of all that 'air and feeding 'em on Dover soles. These two will keep their-selves tidy and eat any damn thing they're given.'

'How much will it all come to, please?'

'You want separate bills, or one'll do, if you're together. Brothers?'

'Yes.'

'Right. Name of?'

'Severs.'

'The masters Severs,' he intoned, scribbling, 'for supplying one aquarium and two kittens. I'll make it out jest to cover me expenses. Now, 'ow much did yer mum give you to spend on this little lot? We can get at the right price that way, I'm sure.'

'She give us, gave us I mean, ten bob.'

'Fair enough. Ten bob it is, and I'll pack 'em all up so they won't bust, free of charge.'

Suckers, swindled once again? Mugs, right charlies, born only to be conned? Yes, thank goodness. Innocence preserved; and whenever I get the worst of a transaction a return of that earlier experience comes to mind, and I rejoice. Surely anything is better than haggling? Besides, I'm really not certain who got the best of that deal. We three were quite satisfied, and I should say that Margaret was the only loser; and yet no more of a loser than she would have been in any case, even if we had managed to cheapen the goods. We should certainly have kept the change. But I see, by reporting an incident in which I behaved with some degree of calmness and dignity, I have merely put off the evil hour of confession to a very different sort of reaction to a situation which, in itself, could have been resolved with compassion and decency.

So, here goes. The next day we were all set to train those cats. I mean, of course, to further their education as acrobats. Cookie taught them soon enough that they could pollute the garden safely, but not her kitchen. At low tide we had planned to fill the aquarium with the ocean, its flora and, if very lucky, its fauna. It came, therefore, as a bitter blow to me (since John was excused) to hear from Margaret that she had arranged a social engagement on my behalf with Joan, the daughter of a spiritualist friend of hers. It put me into a rage at once, under the influence of which I remained until the hour of reckoning released me. (Am I still trying to lay the blame elsewhere? Not altogether; only to establish my mood at the time, and already a certain lack of control.)

'But why should I play golf with Joan?'

'Because she needs fresh air, living in the dark with all those ghosts, and it'll be very good for her; and you should begin to meet girls of your own age, now.'

'If only you knew how boring they are! Can't she get air on the Prom? Besides I've got an important engagement with John. We were going to teach those kittens to climb and also to arrange the aquarium.'

'You can do all that another day, dear.'

'Oh well, curse it, all right. It costs five bob for children.'

I intended to do only nine holes which cost half a crown and the remainder would cover my fee for tuition. I'm not going to describe that round; or half-round to be accurate. Joan was the right shape for tapping a table and only had to lean on it to set it swinging violently. But to swing a golf club effectually the body itself has to be capable of swinging, and that requires muscle not lard. I grant that in the dim light of one of her mother's sessions she would not need the keenest sight to ascertain the position of a table, but on a bright day in August on the West Hove links one might have hoped she would have been able to spot a golf ball. I did my best. I went so far as to take her sweaty hands in my sweatier ones and place them correctly on the club. Even so, and urging her to keep such eyes as she had on the ball, she usually managed to send the turf a good deal further. I've been through some trying engagements in my time but I still think of this one as among the heaviest. For most of it I had bottled up my emotions fairly well, giving Joan twenty strokes a hole, and not counting misses or near misses after an hour's hard labour, we reached the fatal fifth hole all square.

'I think this is a beastly game, Dick.'

'Pretty beastly, yes.'

'I shall never be any good at it.'

'No. But everybody's good at something. You're very hot at getting the dead to talk. They've never said anything to me, yet.'

'That's because you go on thinking of them as dead whereas they're alive.'

'All the same it needs practice, I'll bet, just like golf or any other game.'

'Game? Don't you ever think of anything more serious than games?'

'Hardly ever; and if you're talking about death I'd sooner be alive than one of those spirits. Even a wretched worm would, if it could think at all.'

'Can't you get hold of it? It seems so easy to me. There's no such thing as death. As Mother puts it: in the midst of death we are in life.'

'You could put it the other way round, too. Much the same thing in the long run, but the deaduns win every time as there are more of them.'

'Mother says nothing ever dies.'

'Let's hope so. Mine once said she and I wouldn't, but it didn't cheer me up much. Shall we get on with it? Your honour, I think.'

Here, driving towards the sixth, she positively staggered me with an amazing stroke of fully forty yards even though it was sliced into the rough. We lost sight of the ball and had to search; that is to say I searched and she lightened my work by song:

> I fear no foe with Thee at hand to bless;
> Ills have no weight and tears no bitterness;
> Where is death's sting? Where, Grave, thy victory?
> I triumph still, if Thou abide with me.

Thus encouraged, and scrabbling about with a putter, I found that bloody ball under a gorse bush and chucked it back onto the fairway without charging her a penalty. Decent, especially as the bush, though not unto death, had stung me twice on the back of the neck. But she was not to triumph for long. As she began the last verse of the hymn she broke off with a loud scream.

'Good heavens, what's up now?'

'There! It's coming straight for me. Kill it, kill it.'

I looked up and saw an endless brown rope with black arrow-heads on it – V for victory – intent only on escape.

'All right, get out of the way, then.'

She drew back a bit, and I attacked with the putter. But all snakes move in such a deceptive gliding way that there's no know-ing whereabouts you'll hit them, if at all. I had aimed at the head and struck it on the back; and so it writhed in helpless knots while she shouted: 'Oh, poor snake, poor little snake, you've hurt it dreadfully. Kill it. Put it out of its agony. Kill it quickly.' I had already destroyed its shape and its function for life. The black and brown markings were overlaid with splashes of red, and a thin yellow fluid seeped out of its deeper wounds. I had broken its spinal column and yet it still continued to coil and uncoil. I hacked away with the club, and scales and portions of flesh bespattered the ground; until at last the twisting segments were still. What had I done? I had transmuted a work of beauty and of joy into a grief for ever. And so painful has been the writing of this episode that I shall give myself a grain of satisfaction, here and now. The martyr did not die so cruel a death in vain. Never, since then, has any other snake suffered at my hands. I have come across plenty; and, when they were exposed to danger I have directed them towards the nearest cover. I remember one in particular that, amidst the blaring of horns from impatient motorists, I escorted across the main Haslemere-Chichester road. It took us quite five minutes as one of us made very slow progress on a macadamized surface. But these comforting reflections I apply only as a balm to my con-science and not in mitigation of a murder most foul.

After all that I could not bear the sight of poor old Joan another moment. I sent her packing straight downhill, between the grave-yard and the club-house, the shortest way home to Hova Villas and the sort of life she was used to.

I could be grateful that there was no immediate inquest as, on my return, I found the coroner laid out on a sofa with a sick head-ache. She complained that she always got them in thundery

weather. This was really a myth, and if my mother's health had
begun to give way it could simply be put down to lack of anything
whatever to do. For so active a person she required a lot of exercise to keep her fit. I had hoped to reassure her by declaring that it
was a perfect day and that she could not possibly have heard
thunder. John and I knew well that a gentle breeze from the south-
east brought with it the rumble of guns on the Western Front – and
we told her that was all she had heard. But a *malade imaginaire*
does not like to be restored to health quite so abruptly; and I dare
say we were a trifle unsympathetic. But it stirred the patient
into the sort of response which always confounded those who
attempted to advise her of facts, and certainly proved that she
could not have been at her last gasp. 'As there is thunder about you
will wear your mackintoshes this afternoon.' So, for our well-
meant attentions, we were to be broiled alive; and hooted at by our
friends into the bargain.

In Queen's Gardens, which on that afternoon we rebels entered
suitably clothed in bathing costumes, we were accustomed to
expend superfluous energy in the company of a mixed gang of boys
and girls of all ages. I could have done without the girls. For one
thing they seriously lowered the tone of the organized games I enjoyed so that cricket eventually degenerated into rounders; and we
even had to put up with French cricket with a tennis racket and a
soft ball – not to mention hide-and-seek or twos-and-threes. It was
a shame since we had splendid leaders, Billy and Raymond, both
at Dartmouth, who, if left to themselves, would have chosen their
sides on merit alone; but these rivals in sport, most unfortunately
for me, were inexplicably rivals for the company of a piffling girl.
The only thing I can remember about Irma was that she was tall
and utterly feeble; and yet, whichever one of those two youths won
the toss, she was invariably his first choice and assured, by way of
compensation, that the other lad would win the game whatever it
might be. Both my heroes were about fifteen, and I should think
Irma was much the same sort of age. I see now that it was most
unwise for a junior to have taken it upon himself to try and clean
up Queen's Gardens, and give a sense of purpose to our desultory
play. But how was I to know, in my ignorance and innocence, that
already, among our little band, mysterious complications were at
work to disrupt the accustomed and stereotyped patterns of childhood? Some of my friends had undoubtedly crossed a frontier

which I could not hope to do with a passport that was not yet valid for an extension of my travels. During an interval in the game I tagged on to Billy (whose turn it was to lose) and Irma.

'What about a walk this evening, Irma?'

'I've had enough running about today, Bill. I really don't think I could manage it.'

'Well, I could, Billy, easily. We could go on the pier, too.'

'When I want to go for a walk with you, Dick, I'll let you know. Tag off.'

'Why don't you go for a walk with him? You'd probably be able to go much further as I'd only want to sit down in the first shelter we came to.'

'That would suit me all right. Or, if you'd prefer it we might go to a cinema?'

'She wouldn't care for that, Billy. They've all got that one about Mons, and you know how hopeless girls are about battles and things.'

'Besides, I saw it last night – with Raymond.'

'Oh, blast it all, Dick, can't you clear off? What the hell *do* you want anyway?'

'Nothing much. If you can't go for a walk with me tonight we might have a swim together sometime or other.'

'You'd better fix it up with him, Bill. You won't get rid of him any other way. These kids!'

'All right, then, Dick. Usual place by the groyne at 7.30 a.m. to-morrow; and now make yourself scarce.'

'Thanks awfully, Billy. I'll be there.'

My approach to those youths was radically different from Irma's. I was amazed how reluctant she seemed to be to show the slightest sign of interest in either of them. In my case it was just the other way round. However much I pestered them, they showed not the slightest sign of interest in me; and if she languidly drifted off with one of them I, for my part, had to trot along beside the other to receive any notice at all; and such as I got was generally unsympathetic. In my opinion I was much more decent than she was. I liked them both equally and thought they would be fine chums for a boy like me. She was always attempting to set them at loggerheads. I liked nothing better than to encourage their friend-ship and listen to their manly talk about Dartmouth and the Navy; and it was true that I was tolerated by both of them when nothing better offered. But the social climate was chilling compared with the give and take of Beaudesert. The mere presence of a girl, and moreover one so totally inept at games, sufficed to make pretty good rotters of two otherwise sound and jolly chaps; and I feared for their future careers as admirals. If they dithered about so awkwardly with Irma, how on earth would they behave when confronted with a more formidable enemy? The whole business was rather like a jigsaw puzzle impossible to put together as too many of the pieces were missing.

I was in for a very nasty shock the next morning. It is a disagreeable surprise to discover that one's own most amiable feelings for a fellow human being are by no means always reciprocated. If it is vanity that leads one to expect one's advances will be welcome, then the rejection of them is only wounding to one's self-esteem. But to offer up unqualified love and have it spurned in the most brutal manner leaves one paralysed – especially on a beach at break of day. Bill's greeting to my cheerful approach was a fearful scowl, and I immediately heard him say though I did not take it in, that I was a poisonous little worm fit only to be chopped into pieces, that I had better mind my manners with girls, and that if I had been three years older and nearer his size he would have knocked my block off. He had half a mind to do so, as it was. Irma again; and I admit that I had often disparaged her fielding at cover-point. Was that a crime? Should a technical criticism be allowed to spoil a friendship? He walked off without another word and I was left pondering on the unfairness of everything. I pulled myself together after a bit, and at first recklessly hung around in case Raymond were to turn up. He often did, and I would just as soon have bathed with him as with Bill; but then the thought struck me that if Irma had complained to him, too, my situation would hardly be improved. I was a quick learner and was on the point of scrambling up the beach when another scowling character barred my progress. This one was three years younger than me and not yet my size. I could knock John's block off if necessary and I did not think he was capable of returning the compliment. He was enraged that I had sneaked off without him; and as I was delighted to see him I could afford to apologize. Besides, if Raymond should now turn up and prove as prejudiced as Bill he might think twice about tackling two of us. John had thoughtfully brought our buckets with him; so that, after a refreshing swim, we were able to transport enough of the sea to fill the aquarium. At the same time we had collected sand, a few pebbles and three different kinds of seaweed: a small bit of laver, another of bladder-wrack and a delicate rosy fern-like weed which we felt would be acceptable to any creatures we might later introduce into this comfortable asylum.

When the contents of the tank had subsided we thought at first that we had broken a frond off the fern. But that speck of seaweed was distinctly in motion; and looking closely at it we agreed that it was a rarity of the first order. It was not a common-or-garden crab. Those, also minute and charming, could be found everywhere in their thousands. This one stalked on high stilts and reminded us of pinheaded spiders. Proudly we wrote out a label and stuck it on the aquarium: SPIDER-CRAB (young). Locality: The Big Groyne, Hove Beach, Sussex. August 8. 1915.

I shall end this chapter on an even happier note. Bill and Raymond both came to my thirteenth birthday tea-party. Bill teased the cats to their delight; and Raymond, perhaps more of a lady's man after all, teased Ursula. Later, the four of us went off to look at that shark in the Aquarium – until closing time. John, after watching it circle aimlessly around, asked me if it reminded me of anyone?

'Careful, whisper it.'

'Irma?'

'Yes,' I hissed, 'that's just what I was going to say!'

CHAPTER ELEVEN

Towards the end of August I became aware of a general decline in my morale accompanied by an inability to enjoy even the normal pleasures of life. I felt stale and stuffy. I was not altogether a stranger to such a mood. I think that always, at that season, I was at a particularly low ebb; and I clearly remembered the distress I experienced at Scarborough when, for a moment, by the edge of the sea, I found myself confronted by vast forces which were totally incomprehensible to me. A more recent example comes to mind. At Ford Place I was shattered by the approach of the hounds of the Stracheys. This, too, was at the end of the summer. In later life I was subject to a loss of vitality at the same time of year; and it might be tempting to account for it by a near fatal conjunction of my stars. But while I readily admit to being more than a little superstitious I have never seriously taken into account astrological predictions. I have an hypothesis, and which I like to think is based on science, to account for this annual depression. The time just before birth, and on the day itself, is one of such an expenditure of energy that once the work is over there is for a considerable time only just enough left to keep one alive – and too often not even for that, as is proved by the Registrar General's statistics. I suggest that this seasonal trauma is repeatedly experienced by us all, and I would seriously recommend everybody to take things easily for a month or two either side of the fatal anniversary.

But this year, for the first time, my uneasiness was reinforced by recent discomforting experiences at Beaudesert which had also made their presence felt in Hove. The world I was used to seemed to be disintegrating. The old responses no longer brought relief. In place of the traditional and carefree reactions to events which, shared by others, more than sufficed to give me an anonymous sense of the normal, I began to feel myself cast adrift on a sea of insecurity tossed about by huge waves that threatened to overwhelm me, as in those far off days of infancy when I was a prey to the wildest passions.

I was not, of course, conscious that I was approaching another change in my mental and physical being. I was, however, scared and bewildered at the strength and depth of passions which had not made their presence felt, or only slightly, since the nightmare world of infancy. I could not understand that I, so tender in my personal dealings with other forms of life (except certain species of insects – an acquired and habitual hostility deriving from my Indian days) should have behaved with such brutal ferocity towards the snake on the golf course. I was shocked at the thought that I was capable of an act of senseless cruelty. And I was just as much disturbed at my rejection by Bill on the beach. Why should I suddenly take such an incident so much to heart? Chums had come and gone at regular intervals at Beaudesert Park without leaving any emotional distress behind them; and yet now I felt disgraced and humiliated. It seemed to me that the world which up to then had been small and friendly had, almost overnight, fearfully expanded and was revealed as containing quite as many inexplicable horrors as those I had left behind me in the nursery. I began to withdraw from the communal life of Hove, and one blustery day early in September I got on my bicycle and headed for the Downs; either in the hope that, alone, I might be able to sort out these new complications, or more simply that the emotional cobwebs might themselves be blown away and leave me so refreshed that, on my return from the mountain, I should once again be able to see the world with which I was familiar.

As I turned away from the Dyke I came into the full force of the gale; and my sole preoccupation was not to get blown off the track and to make progress whenever the storm abated. I was encouraged by the thought of a speed record on the return journey, and comforted to know that the wind would not reach the bottom of the dells, in one of which I intended to have my lunch. These hollows, like pock marks on the smooth skin of the Downs, were not formed by supernatural agencies. They were the work of knappers who dug down into the chalk in search of flints and are to be found all over the south of England.

After some two miles of hard labour I found the first of these hollows, a large specimen which was well-known to me. With wings outstretched and body inclined over the side I preserved, as I had hoped would be the case, a long moment of delicious inertia, poised for flight but balanced between the power that tugged me to descend and the wind that upheld me: a battle of the elements for the boy-bird that was at last won by the more constant force. As I raced down the slope, my strides so lengthening that I did, at times, seem to be flying, I let out a wild yell to warn the bunnies of the swoop of an eagle or at least of a sparrow. But there was no response. Not one was to be seen; and this would have been a disappointment and a mystery had I not observed towards the end of my descent that I had flushed larger game: a man, with a bundle of papers under one arm, scurried away for shelter, and I then, for the first time, noticed a tiny wisp of smoke rising from a small fire over which he had apparently been crouching. Eventually, reassured I suppose at the sight of nothing more sinister than a boy, he emerged cautiously from the bushes and sat down beside me.

I should not have ventured to disturb a family gathering of Didicoy, nor the privacy of my present companion if I had spotted him from the heights. But he was a small man wearing an outsize brown Homburg hat. Foreshortened and hidden under the hat he was practically invisible; and I could be forgiven for mistaking that article for the back of an old rabbit. From the very beginning of our encounter he proved to be far more sociable than I, though I warmed to him later on.

'Well, old boy, since you're here, welcome to the office. Excuse me for rushing off like that, but I had no engagements this morning and I thought it was wiser to clear off until I had a chance to see who my visitor might be. Let me introduce myself: Mr John Crook, business consultant. Here, read this envelope.'

I read aloud: 'Señor Don Juan Crook' (with an address in Shoreham).

'Oh dear, not Juan, please. Hhuan is correct.'

'Huan.'

'Hhuan' (a sort of gargle).

I gave up. 'Welsh?'

'No, Spanish. An Anglo-Spanish business man, stranded, alas, in your country by the outbreak of war; and deprived of an honest living by the officious attentions of his landlady. I assure you, my dear sir, she's taken to steaming open my letters, deleting all the important parts, and then closing them up again, so that it looks as if they've come to me straight from abroad. Just read this one, will you? All the information a business man requires neatly blacked out.'

I read:

'Dear Mr Crook,
With reference to my last of the 17th: censored tons of censored will now be delivered at censored as required. Kindly get in touch with our associates in censored and urge instant dispatch to censored.
Yours, etc.,
censored.'

'I ask you, could anyone make head or tail of that?'

'I suppose you could look up that letter of the 17th?'

'Naturally I did that. But the whole letter has been blacked out so that it reads: "Dear Mr Crook, yours truly." '

He tossed the two letters with their envelopes into the fire.

'I ask you! What on earth can the old wretch be after?'

'Sorry, it's beyond me. But surely it's a waste of time to destroy the stamps? South American, all of them, and my collection is very weak on those countries.'

'Collect stamps, do you? By the bye, what's *your* name?'

'Dick.'

'Well then, Dick, we can get a little work done in the office, after all. Partners, eh? You tear off the stamps and then hand over the letters and envelopes for me to burn. And if you finish before I do you might collect a few more twigs to keep up the fire. Cold for the time of year.'

We polished off the arrears of correspondence before lunch which, in return for the stamps, I had the decency to share with him. After dredging up this strange encounter, I have come to the conclusion that his 'landlady' acted too precipitately; or perhaps she was just softening him up. If he were totally deprived of any means of communication with his overseas friends, they would sooner or later cease to write to him; and many cargoes, without his useful information, might slip through our hands and eventually reach central Europe. But perhaps she realized this in time, and allowed uncensored letters to reach him, and others to escape unharmed from his office. No doubt, if this were so, unsuspectingly, and rather ironically, he might have observed one or more of his own convoys destined for a neutral port safely escorted into Shoreham harbour by the Navy. In the end, when of no further use, I suppose he was quietly put away for the duration on a minor charge such as being without visible means of support; and I trust that nothing worse happened to him. I feel fairly confident that consideration for his services to the country would have been taken into account. I am still aware now of my strong sympathy for a fellow sufferer, though his problems were of a more materialistic nature than mine. And if I should be considered too kindly, in this instance, to yet another enemy agent, I was impressed by the mildness of the Anglo-Spanish variety compared with the brutality of the Anglo-Swiss. It must be remembered that the bread and salt had passed between us and, not least, that in discussing his predicament I had been, temporarily, relieved of mine. I have faithfully recorded this picnic party: an odd story so far as it went – but I like stories to end; and I must apologize for leaving it in the air. That is exactly how we left each other. From the opposite rims of the crater, we waved goodbye; he, clutching his hat, to face it all the way to Shoreham; I, on my bicycle, to be swept before it down to Hove.

I'm aware that, in this chapter so far, I have been far less positive than usual. Moods have come and gone, stories have been begun and left unfinished – and, by way of apology, I can only offer the explanation that some of the uncertainties of that period of my life have risen to the surface and have reproduced themselves once again in the telling. These discomforts continued at Beaudesert. The old gang was not allowed to proceed on its anonymous course. Arthur Harry fished us out from the sheltering seaweed; and we became conspicuously visible. Some such as Sooty, rare specimens indeed, were considered as possible scholars and were subject to long hours of private coaching. But even the rest of us were constantly harassed by the study of old examination papers which, it was considered, might prepare us for passing the Common Entrance. I was unwise enough to boast that any fool could pass it easily. For a short time I was advanced to deal with the same sort of papers as those inspected by Sooty. But, as Sir pointed out, a satisfactory translation of Caesar or Tacitus did not qualify one to render into English the subtle ramifications of Cicero's correspondence or the even profounder philosophy of such works as *De Natura Rerum* – at least not into English that made sense. As far as the Scholarship Stakes were concerned I was soon declared a non-runner; and even my French, in the lesser division, was held to be suspect; entirely due to the Baron's illegible writing. In this instance telescopic sights would have been a great help. He, too, was engaged on these papers. Henri was not destined for an English public school; but, old fashioned as it may sound, for the cavalry at Saumur. He required a horse, not a pen. His father was away with his regiment and could not be consulted. Sir did his best for Froggie and bought him a bicycle – not the same thing, though it may have given him a sense of balance. In any case, by the time he reached that military school we can guess that *les dragons* had been superseded by *les chars*; and so, once again, Mr Richardson, introducing this difficult pupil to the mysteries of machinery, had proved himself to be more than competent to direct even a foreign youth in the way he might be expected to go.

As seniors, however, and segregated from lesser fry, we had the small dormitory to ourselves. During the whole of that last year we were still able to recapture, before one or other of us, whose turn of duty it was, blew out the candle, much of that spirit of solidarity which had prevailed in earlier times. Naturally we engaged with the same enthusiasm in all the old rituals of life at Beaudesert Park. They were very dear to us; but I shall not need to linger over them as I believe I have given them on other pages the importance they deserved and an adequate representation. Out of that welcome continuation, which must always be borne in mind, there arose new curiosities and wild speculations concerning the life to come. We could question but not answer. And the subjects were by general consent considered too dangerous to be brought to adult notice – I still don't think our enquiries would have met with a full and truthful response anyhow, as increasingly they turned on the biological functions of the human body and more especially on the propagation of the species.

The little dormitory, then, was inhabited by Sooty, Fabian, David, myself and the odd man out, Henri. The four of us knew, a year before the event, that we were destined for Rugby. Henri was generously thrown in among us to lighten the encircling gloom, and possibly to bring us along in French conversation. With regard to Sooty someone had blundered badly. His talents and eccentricities would have been more speedily understood and accepted at Eton – though, eventually, they were more or less tolerated at Rugby. He was sorely tried in his early days, but his brains rapidly promoted him into the Sixth, and in that haven he was naturally spared the inconveniences the rest of us had to endure as best we could. David, Fabian and I, without protection of any sort, were thrown to the wolves (though I recklessly and, as it turned out, falsely promised my chums Big Cousin).

Vincent, my cousin, had been sent to Rugby. He not only survived but rose to become Head of the School – a position in which, I suppose, my deluded relatives hoped I might follow him; or that, under the wing of such an important figure, it would be considered too dangerous for others to relieve their frustrations on my person. That latter hope might have been realized if Vincent, when I arrived, had still been there. But he had left the term before. As usual the Stracheys and those connected with them had acted as if Time stood still. Perhaps it did for them; yet they should have perceived it did not do so for lesser mortals, and that it ticked on as relentlessly for Heads of Schools as for new boys. Vincent's feelings for Rugby were similar to mine for Beaudesert Park, incredible as it may sound. He returned, during my first term there, to gossip with his successor, to recapture some of his old happiness and if not exactly to stop the clock to put it back a month or two. He had a warm heart and found time, from more important engagements, to invite his miserable little cousin to a magnificent breakfast at the George. Thanks awfully, Cousin Vincent! You certainly could not have imagined how much such a meal had in common with that provided for the prisoner before his melancholy march to the scaffold.

There is only one concession I am prepared to make for Rugby – I should have been just as unhappy at any other public school.